CW00859656

MANX FAIRY TALES

SECOND EDITION.

PEEL:
Published by
L. MORRISON,
1929.

PUBLISHER'S NOTE

It is eighty years since the first edition of *Manx Fairy Tales* appeared combining in one volume many of the traditional tales which have become part of Manx folk-lore. A second edition appeared in 1929 with additional stories and this time enriched with characteristic illustrations by the famous Manx artist Archibald Knox. This edition was reprinted by the Manx Museum and National Trust in 1971. The time has now come for a second reprint which it is hoped will help perpetuate the original work of Sophia Morrison and provide pleasure for future generations.

Gordon N. Kniveton
March, 1991

ISBN 1873120 01 X

This edition is published by The Manx Experience, 10 Tromode Close, Douglas, Isle of Man in association with the Manx Museum and National Trust.

Printed by Alden Press Ltd., Osney Mead, Oxford.

PREFACE

THERE is at least one spot in the world where Fairies are still believed in, and where, if you look in the right places, they may still be found, and that is the little island from which these stories come—Ellan Vannin, the Isle of Mann. But I have used a word which should not be mentioned here —they are never called Fairies by the Manx, but Themselves, or the Little People, or the Little Fellows, or the Little Ones, or sometimes even the Lil' Boys. These Little People are not the tiny creatures with wings who flutter about in many English Fairy tales, but they are small persons from two to three feet in height, otherwise very like mortals. They wear red caps and green jackets and are very fond of hunting—indeed they are most often seen on horseback followed by packs of little hounds of all colours of the rainbow. They are rather inclined to be mischievous and spiteful, and that is why they are called by such good names, in case they should be listening!

Besides these red-capped Little Fellows there are other alarming folk. There is the Fynoderee, who is large, ugly, hairy and enormously strong, but not so bad as he looks, for often he helps on the farm during the night by thrashing corn. He does not like to be seen, so if a farmer wants work done by him, he must take care to keep out of the Fynoderee's way. Then, far uglier than Fynoderee, are the Bugganes, who are horrible and cruel creatures. They can appear in any shape they please—as ogres with huge heads and great fiery eyes, or without any heads at all; as small dogs who grow larger and larger as you watch them until they are larger than elephants, when perhaps they turn into the shape of men or disappear into nothing; as horned monsters or anything they choose. Each Buggane has his own particular dwelling-place—a dark sea-cave, a lonely hill, or a ruined Keeill, or Church. There are many others too, but these are the chief.

Most of the stories are traditional and have been handed down by word of mouth from father to son. I owe hearty thanks to those from whose lips I have heard them —Messrs. J. R. Moore, William Cashen, Joe Moore, Ned Quayle and others. Of the four stories which have not been told to me personally—Teeval, The Wizard's Palace, Kitterland, and Smereree—the three first have been printed in various folk-lore books, and the Manx of the last appeared in ***Yn Lioar Manninagh*** some years ago. Lastly I must thank my friend Miss Alice Williams for her kind help and valuable assistance in many ways.

SOPHIA MORRISON.

PEEL, ISLE OF MANN,
October, 1911.

Since the Preface was written the following stories have been included in the book :—

Story	*Source.*
TEHI TEGI	*Waldron.*
THE MODDEY DOO . .	*Waldron.*
THE CITY UNDER SEA . .	*Waldron.*
KING MAGNUS BAREFOOT .	*Chronicon Manniae.*
THE BUGGANE OF S. TRINIAN'S	Well-known traditional tale found in all Guide Books.

Preface to Second Edition

THE first edition of this book has been out of print for some years, and, as there has been a constant demand for copies, it has been thought advisable to issue another edition and, at the same time, add a few more tales and folk-lore notes from my sister's unpublished work.

This new edition has been enriched with characteristic illustrations by the well-known artist, Mr. Archibald Knox. His clever work beautifies the pages and also interprets their spirit. I take this opportunity of expressing my gratitude to him for his very generous gift. I wish also to thank Mr. J. J. Kneen for his kindness in reading and correcting the Manx proofs and finally Mr. L. G. Meyer for all the trouble and care he has taken in the printing of the book to make it as perfect as possible.

L. MORRISON.

PEEL,
November, 1929.

CONTENTS

Manx Fairy Tales.

I

THERE was a man once in the Isle of Mann who met one of the Little Fellows, and the Little Fellow told him that if he would go to London Bridge and dig, he would find a fortune. So he went, and when he got there he began to dig, and another man came to him and said:

'What are you doing?'

'One of Themselves told me to come to London Bridge and I would get a fortune,' says he. And the other man said:

'I dreamed that I was back in the lil' islan' an' I was at a house with a thorn-tree at the chimley of it, and if I would dig there I would find a fortune. But I wouldn' go, for it was only foolishness.'

Then he told him so plainly about the house that the first man knew it was his own, so he went back to the Island. When he got home he dug under the little thorn-tree by the chimney and he found an iron box. He opened the box and it was full of gold, and there was a letter in it, but he could not read the letter because it was in a foreign language. So he put it in the smithy window and challenged any scholar who went by to read it. None of them could, but at last one big boy said it was Latin and it meant:

'Dig again and you'll find another.'

So the man dug again under the thorn-tree, and what did he find but another iron box full of gold!

And from that day till the day of his death, that man used to open the front door before going to bed, and call out: 'My blessing with the Little Fellows!'

II

IS A TRUE STORY that was told to me by a man named James Moore when I was sitting with him by the fire one evening. He said: 'I'm not much of a believer in most of the stories some ones is telling, but after all a body can't help believing a thing they happen to see for themselves.

'I remember one winter's night—we were living in a house at the time that was pulled down for the building of the Big Wheel. It was a thatched house with two rooms, and a wall about six foot high dividing them, and from that it was open to the scrahs, or turfs, that were laid across the rafters. My Mother was sitting at the fire busy spinning, and my Father was sitting in the big chair at the end of the table taking a chapter for us out of the Manx Bible. My brother was busy winding a spool and I was working with a bunch of ling, trying to make two or three pegs.

'"There's a terrible glisther on to-night," my Mother said, looking at the fire. "An' the rain comin' peltin' down the chimley!"

'"Yes," said my Father, shutting the Bible; "an' we better get to bed middlin' soon and let the Lil' Ones in to a bit of shelter."

'So we all got ready and went to bed.

'Some time in the night my brother wakened me with a:

'"Sh—ish! Listen boy; an' look at the big light tha's in the kitchen!" Then he rubbed his eyes a bit and whispered;

'"What's mother doin' now at all?"

'"Listen!" I said. "An' you'll hear mother in bed, it's not her at all; it must be the Little Ones that's agate of the wheel!"

'And both of us got frightened, and down with our heads under the clothes and fell asleep. In the morning when we got up we told them what we had seen, first thing.

'"Aw, like enough, like enough," my Father said, looking at the wheel. "It seems your mother forgot to take the band off last night, a thing people should be careful about, for it's givin' Themselves power over the wheel, an' though their meanin's well enough, the spinnin' they're doin' is nothin' to brag about. The weaver is always shoutin' about their work an' the bad joinin' they're makin' in the rolls."

'"I remember it as well as yesterday— the big light that was at them, and the whirring that was going on. And let anybody say what they like, that's a thing I've seen and heard for myself."'

III

One evening a young man who was serving his time as a weaver was walking home late from Douglas to Glen Meay. He had often been boasting that he had never seen any of the Little People. Well, this night he was coming along the St. John's Road, and when he got near to the river a big, big bull stood across the road before him. He took his stick and gave it one big knock. It went into the river and he never saw it any more.

After that, when he got to the Parson's Bridge, he met a little thing just like a spinning wheel and there was a little, little body sitting where the spool is. Well, he lifted his stick again and struck the little body that was sitting on the spool a hard knock with his stick. The little body said to him:

'Ny jean shen arragh!' which means, 'Don't do that again!'

He walked on then till he got to Glen Meay and told what he had seen in a house there. Then another man said he had seen the little old woman sitting on the top of the spool of the spinning wheel and coming down Raby Hill at dark. So it took her a long time, for the first man met her at six and the second at eleven, and there is'nt two miles between the two places.

So they were saying, when the cycles came in, that the Little People had been before them! And this is a true story.

THE BUGGANE of GLEN MEAY WATERFALL

WAS ONCE a woman living near Glen Meay, and she was the wife of a decent, quiet, striving man of the place. There was no one but herself and the man, and they had a nice little cottage and owned a bit of a croft on which they grazed a cow and a few sheep and grew enough potatoes to do them the winter out; and the man had a yawl and went to the fishing when things were slack on land. But for all that they were not comfortable, for work as hard as the man might at his farming and his fishing, he was kept as poor as Lazarus by a lazy wife.

For the woman was fonder of lying a-bed in the morning than sitting at her milking stool; indeed the neighbours had it to say that she wore out more blankets than shoes. Many a day her man would be going out early as hungry as a hawk, without a bite or a sup in him. One morning when he came in from work for his breakfast there was no fire—his wife was never up. Well my poor man had nothing for it but to get his own breakfast ready and go back to his work. When he came in for dinner it happened as it had happened for breakfast.

'Bad luck to her laziness,' he thought; 'this is coul comfort for a poor man, but I'll play a trick on her for it.'

And with that he fetched a bart of straw and bunged the two windows of his house. Then he went back to his work.

The sun had not yet set when he came home in the evening. His wife was lying in bed waiting for day.

'Aw, woman,' he shouted, 'make haste an' get up to see the sun rise in the wes'.'

Up jumped the wife and ran to the door just as the sun was going down, and the sight terrified her. The whole sky looked like fire, and she thought that the end of the world had come. But next morning it all happened as it had happened before, and himself said to her:

'Kirry, it's the Buggane, sure enough, that'll be having thee one of these days if thou don't mend thy ways!'

'What Buggane?' said she.

'Ax me no questions,' said he, 'an' I'll tell thee no lies. But it's the big, black, hairy fellow that lies under the Spooyt Vooar that I'm meaning'.'

'Aw, houl yer tongue, man; thou don't frecken me wi' thy Bugganes,' shouted the woman.

In the evening the man left the house to go out to the fishing. As soon as he had gone the woman took a notion in her head to bake, as she had only the heel o' the loaf left for breakfast. Now, Themselves can't stand lazy ways, and baking after sunset is the one thing they won't abide. She who does so will meet their revenge—something is sure to be taken by them, but seldom worse than some of the live stock. Well, the woman set to work to bake some barley bread and flour cake. First, she went out to get gorse to put under the griddle, slipping the bolt on the door as she came in, that none of the neighbours would catch her and cry shame on her for baking after sunset. She got some meal out of the barrel and put it on the round table, and put salt and water on it, and then she kneaded the meal and clapped a cake out as thin as sixpence with her hands. But she was only a middling poor baker, one of the sort that has to use a knife to make the cake of a right round. She had turned the cake twice, and taken it off, and brushed the griddle with a white goose wing ready for the next cake which she was busy cutting round with her knife. Just at that moment there was heard the sound of something heavy lumbering up to the door. After a few seconds SOME-

THING fumbled at the sneg of the door, then SOMETHING knocked high up on the door, and a voice like the thick, gruff voice of a giant was heard saying, 'Open, open for me.' She made no answer. Again there was a loud knock and a big hoarse voice was heard which cried: 'Woman of the house, open for me.' Then the door burst open and behold ye, what should she see but a great, big ugly beast of a Buggane rushing in mad with rage. Without as much as a 'By your leave,' he made one grab at her, and clutched hold of her by her apron and swung her on his shoulder, and away with him. Before she knew where she was he rushed her across the fields and down the hill, till he brought her to the top of the Spooyt Vooar, the big waterfall of Glen Meay. As the Buggane tore down the hill, the woman felt the ground tremble under his feet, and the noise of the waterfall filled her ears. And, there in front of her, she saw the stream turn to white spray as it came leaping down the rocks. As the Buggane swung her in the air to throw her into the deep pool, she thought that her last hour had come. Then all at once she remembered the knife that she held in her hand! Quick as thought she cut the string of her apron and down she tumbled to the ground, rolling over and over down the hill. And before he knew where he was, the Buggane, with the speed he had on him, pitched forward head first down the rushing Spooyt Vooar. As he went head over heels and down to the bottom of the pool with a souse you'd have heard half-a-mile away, she heard him give a roar out of him:

> Rumbyl, rumbyl, sambyl,
> I thought I had a lazy Dirt,
> And I have but the edge of her skirt.

And that was the last that was seen of that fellow!

HOW THE MANX CAT LOST HER TAIL

NOAH WAS calling the animals into the Ark, there was one cat who was out mousing and took no notice when he was calling to her. She was a good mouser, but this time she had trouble to find a mouse and she took a notion that she wouldn't go into the Ark without one.

So at last, when Noah had all the animals safe inside, and he saw the rain beginning to fall, and no sign of her coming in, he said:

'Who's out is out, and who's in is in!' And with that he was just closing the door when the cat came running up, half drowned—that's why cats hate the water—and just squeezed in, in time. But Noah had slammed the door as she ran in and it cut off her tail, so she got in without it, and that is why Manx cats have no tails to this day. That cat said:

Be bo bend it,
My tail's ended,
And I'll go to Mann
And get copper nails,
And mend it.

THOUSANDS of years ago, at the time of the Battles of the Giants in Ireland, Finn Mac Cooil was fighting with a great, red-haired Scotch giant who had come over to challenge him. He beat him, and chased him eastwards towards the sea. But the Scotch giant was a faster runner and began to get ahead of him, so Finn, who was afraid that he would jump into the sea and escape, stooped down and clutched a great handful of the soil of Ireland to throw at him. He cast it, but he missed his enemy, and the great lump of earth fell into the midst of the Irish Sea. It is the Isle of Mann, and the great hole which Finn made, where he tore it up, is Lough Neagh.

There were men, too, in Ireland in those days as well as giants, and to some of them it seemed to happen in a different way. Men do not always understand the doings of giants, because men live, it may be said, in the footprints of the giants. It seems that at this time the Irish tribes were gathered in two great forces getting ready to meet the plunderers who had left Scotland and were at work on their own coast. Their blood got too hot and they went into each other in downright earnest, to show how they would do with the rascals when they came. To their confusion, for they lost hold over themselves, they got into boggy ground and were in great danger. The leaders, seeing that it was going to mean a big loss of life, got all their men together on a big patch of dry ground that happened to be in the bog-land, when all of a sudden a darkness came overhead and the ground began to shake and tremble with the weight of the people and the stir there was at them, and then it disappeared, people and all. Some said that it took a plunge and sank into the bog with the people on it. Others said that it was lifted up, and the people on it dropped off into the swamp. No doubt the darkness that was caused by the hand of Finn made it hard to see just how it happened. However that may be, a while after this they said the sea was surging dreadful, and the men in the boats had to hold to the sides, or it's out they'd have been thrown. And behold ye, a few days after this there was land seen in the middle of the sea, where no man ever saw the like before.

You may know that this story is true because the Irish have always looked on the Isle of Mann as a parcel of their own land. They say that when Saint Patrick put the blessing of God on the soil of Ireland and all creatures that might live upon it, the power of that blessing was felt at the same time in the Island.

> Saint Patrick was a mighty man,
> He was a Saint so clever,
> He gave the snakes and toads a twisht!
> And banished them for ever.

And there is proof of the truth of the saying to this day, for while such nasty things do live in England they cannot breathe freely on the blessed soil.

The island was much larger then than it is now, but the magician who for a time ruled over it, as a revenge on one of his enemies, raised a furious wind in the air and in the bosom of the earth. This wind tore several pieces off the land and cast them into the sea. They floated about and were changed into the dangerous rocks which are now so much feared by ships. The smaller pieces became the shifting sands which wave round the coast, and are sometimes seen and sometimes disappear. Later the island was known as Ellan Sheaynt, the Isle of Peace, or the Holy Island. It was a place where there was always sunshine, and the singing of birds, the scent of sweet flowers, and apple-trees blossoming the whole year round. There was always enough there to eat and drink, and the horses of that place were fine and the women beautiful.

The Coming of Saint Patrick.

TWAS the time that Saint Patrick was coming on horseback to Mann, over the sea from Ireland. When he drew near to the land, Manannan Mac y Leirr, that great wizard that was ruler of Mann, put a charm out of him that made the air round the island thick with mist, so that neither sun nor sky nor sea nor land could be seen. Patrick rode into the thick of the mist, but try as he would he could find no way out of it, and behind him there was a great sea-beast waiting to swallow him up. He didn't know in his seven senses where he was—east, or west—and was for turning back, when there came to his ears the cry of a curlew, calling :

'Come you, come you, come you!'

Then he said to himself :

'The curlew will be down feeding among the rocks; she will be calling to her young.'

After that he heard the bleat of a goat:

'Beware, beware, beware!'

And he said to himself:

'Where the goat bleats for the fall of her kid there will be a steep bit of a hill.'

Last of all he heard the crow of a cock:

'Come to us—come, come!'

Then said Patrick:

'I believe on me sowl I'm back of Peel Hill.'

And with that he took one leap on to the little island and put his horse up the sheer rock. Soon he stood, sure enough, at the top of Peel Hill. As he stood there he cried out:

'Me blessing on the curlew. No man afther this is to find her nest!'

'Me blessing on the goat, an' no man is to see her bring forth her young!'

'Me blessing on the cock, an' he shall crow at dawn ever afther at this same hour!'

He cursed the sea beast and turned him into a solid rock and there he lies now with his great fin on his back.

Where the horse's hoofs struck the top of the hill there sprang a well of pure water, of which man and horse drank, and it is called the Holy Well of Saint Patrick to this day. If you go down to the ledges of the rock, which were made by the horse's hoofs as he clambered up, you may see the footprints still.

When Patrick looked about him the mist was lifting, and he saw a great host of warriors round Manannan's Faery Mound, with the first rays of the rising sun shining on their spears. But the saint knew that they were phantoms raised by Manannan's magic power and he bade them to be gone.

And, behold, they and their master, in the shape of three-legged men, whirled round and round like wheels before the swift wind, which could not overtake them, till they came to Spanish Head. There they whirled over the houghs so quickly and lightly that the gulls on the ledges below were not disturbed, then on over the rough, grey Irish Sea till they came to the enchanted island, fifteen miles south-west of the Calf. Once there Manannan dropped the isle to the bottom of the sea, and he and his company were seen no more.

Saint Patrick on his snow-white horse stood still on Peel Hill and blessed the island where he had touched land, and blessed it has been to this day. Then he leapt on to the little islet that he saw below him. Ever since it has been called Saint Patrick's Isle, and from the rocks on its northern side he watched the fierce storm which Manannan's going had made. Just then a brave ship, with foresail and mainsail gone, was driving straight for the terrible rocks. Saint Patrick raised his mailed hand and the tempest was calmed. The good ship righted herself again, and those on board were saved. They looked up with awe and thankfulness at the rider in his shining armour on the snow-white steed, standing bright against the blackness of the rocks. And ever since that day the fisherman, as he sails past the Horse Rock, has offed with his cap and put up this bit of a prayer to good Saint Patrick:

Saint Patrick, who blessed our Island, bless us and
our boat,
Going out well, coming in better,
With living and dead in the boat.

THE HERRING BECAME KING OF THE SEA

THE old fishermen of the island have it to say that years and years ago the fish met to choose themselves a king, for they had no deemster to tell them what was right. Likely enough their meeting-place was off the Shoulder, south of the Calf. They all came looking their best—there was Captain Jiarg, the Red Gurnet, in his fine crimson coat; Grey Horse, the Shark, big and cruel; the Bollan in his brightest colours; Dirty Peggy, the Cuttle-fish, putting her nicest face on herself; Athag, the Haddock, trying to rub out the black spots the devil burnt on him when he took hold of him with his finger and thumb, and all the rest. Each one thought he might be chosen.

The Fish had a strong notion to make Brac Gorm, the Mackerel, king. He knew that, and he went and put beautiful lines and stripes on himself—pink and green and gold, and all the colours of the sea and sky. Then he was thinking diamonds of himself. But when he came he looked that grand that they didn't know him. So they said that he was artificial and would have nothing to do with him.

In the end it was Skeddan, the Herring, the Lil Silver Fella, who was made King of the sea.

When it was all over, up came the Fluke, too late to give his vote, and they all called out:

'You've missed the tide, my beauty!'

It seems that he had been so busy tallivating himself up, touching himself up red in places, that he forgot how time went. When he found that the herring had been chosen, he twisted up his mouth on one side, and says he:

'An' what am I goin' to be then?'

'Take that,' says Scarrag the Skate, and he ups with his tail and gives the Fluke a slap on his mouth that knocked his mouth crooked on him. And so it has been ever since.

And, maybe, it's because the Herring is King of the Sea that he has so much honour among men. Even the deemsters, when they take their oath, say: 'I will execute justice as indifferently as the herring's back-bone doth lie in the midst of the fish.'

And the Manx people will not burn the herring's bones in the fire, in case the herring should feel it. It is to be remembered, too, that the best herring in the world are caught in this place off the Shoulder, where the fish held their big meeting, and that is because it is not very far from Manannan's enchanted island.

THERE was once a man living in the south of the island whose name was Colcheragh. He was a farmer, and he had poultry on his street, sheep on the mountain, and cattle in the meadow land alongside the river.

His cows were the best cows in the parish. Nowhere could you see such a fine head of cattle as he had ; they were the pride of his heart, and they served him well with milk and butter.

But after a time he began to think that something was amiss with the cows. He went to the cow-house the first thing every morning, and one morning he noticed the cows looking so tired they could hardly stand. When it came to milking time they found not a drop of milk. The girls, who went out to milk the cows ,came back with empty cans, saying:

'The milk has gone up into the cows' horns!'

Colcheragh began to think that some one had put an evil eye on his cows, so he swept up some of the dust from the cross four-roads close by, in a shovel, and sprinkled it on their backs. But the cows got no better. Then he wondered if some one was coming at night to steal the milk. He made up his mind to sit in the cow-house all night to see if he could catch the thief.

So one night after everyone had gone to bed he crept out of the house and hid himself under some straw in a corner of the cow-house. Hour after hour of the dark lonesome night crept on, and he heard nothing but the cows' breathing and their rustle in the straw. He was very cold and stiff, and he had just made up his mind to go into the house, when a glimmering light showed under the door; and then he heard Things laughing and talking—queer talk—he knew that they were not right people. The cow-house door opened and in came a whole lot of Little Men, dressed in green coats and leather caps. Keeking through the straw, he saw their horns hung by their sides, their whips in their hands, and scores of little dogs of every colour—green, blue, yellow, scarlet, and every colour you can think of—at their heels. The cows were lying down. The Little Fellows loosed the yokes from the cows' necks, hopped on their backs, a dozen, maybe, on each cow, and cracked their little whips. The cows jumped to their feet, and Themselves galloped off!

Colcheragh ran to the stable, got on a horse, and made chase after his cows. The night was dark, but he could hear the whizz of the little whips through the air, the click of the cows' hoofs on stones, and the little dogs going:

'Yep, yep, yep!'

He heard, too, the laughing, of Themselves. Then one of them would be singing out to the dogs, calling them up by name, giving a call out of him:

'Ho la, ho la, la!'

Colcheragh followed these sounds, keeping close at their heels, On and on they went, helter-skelter over hedges and over ditches till they got to the Fairy Hill, and Colcheragh was still following them, though on any other night he would not have gone within a mile of the great green mound. When the Little Fellows came to the hill they sounded a tan-ta-ra-ra-tan on their horns. The hill opened, bright light streamed out, and sounds of music and great merriment. Themselves passed through, and Colcheragh slid off his horse and slipped unnoticed in after them. The hill closed behind them and he found himself in a fine room, lit up till it was brighter than the summer noonday. The whole place was crowded with Little People, young and old, men and women, all decked out for a ball, that grand—he had never looked on the like. Among them were some faces that he thought he had seen before, but he took no notice of them, nor they of him. In one part there was dancing to the music of Hom Mooar—that was the name of the fiddler—and when he played all men must follow him whether they would or no. The dancing was like the dancing of flowers in the wind, such dancing as he had never seen before.

In another part his cows were being killed and roasted, and after the dance there was a great feast, with scores of tables set out with silver and gold and everything of the best to eat and drink. There was roast and boiled, and sollaghan and cowree, and puddings and pies, and jough and wine—a feast fit for the Governor himself. When they were taking their seats one of them, whose face he thought he knew, whispered to him: 'Don't thee taste nothin' here or thou will be like me, and never go back to thy ones no more.'

Colcheragh made up his mind to take this advice. When the feast was coming to an end there was a shout for the Jough-y-dorrys, the Stirrup Cup. Some one ran to fetch the cup. The one among the Little People, who seemed to be their king, filled it with red wine, drank himself, and passed it on to the rest. It was going round from one to another until it came to Colcheragh, who saw, when he had it in his hands, that it was of fine carved silver, and more beautiful than anything ever seen outside that place. He said to himself: 'The little durts have stolen and killed and eaten my cattle—this cup, if it were mine, would pay me for all.' So standing up and grasping the silver cup tightly in his hand, he held it up and said:

'Shoh Slaynt!' which is the Manx toast.

Then he dashed the cupful of wine over Themselves and the lights. In an instant the place was in black darkness, save for a stime of grey dawn light which came through the chink of the half-closed door. Colcheragh made for it, cup in hand, slammed the door behind him, and ran for his life.

After a moment of uproar Themselves missed the cup and Colcheragh, and with yells of rage they poured out of the hill after him, in full chase. The farmer, who had a good start, ran as he had never run before. He knew he would get small mercy at their hands if he was caught; he went splashing through the wet mire and keeping off the stepping stones; he knew they could not take him in the water. He looked over his shoulder and caught a glimpse of the whole Mob Beg behind him, close at his heels, waving their naked arms in the light of the torch each one held up. On they came, shrieking and howling in Manx:

> Colcheragh, Colcheragh,
> Put thy foot on the stone,
> And do not put it in the wet!

But he ran in the water till he came to the churchyard, and they could not touch him there. When he went into the cowhouse the next morning the cows had all come home and they got rest after that.

He put the cup in the Church at Rushen, and they are saying it was there for many years; then it was sent to London. It is said that after this the farmer would not go out of his house of an evening after dark.

It was many and many a year ago that the heiress of Eary Cushlin Farm had a little child. Eary Cushlin is a terribly lonely place; it stands high up on the Eanin Mooar, the big precipice, close by the steep brow of Cronk-yn-Irree-Laa. You might live there for months without seeing the face of clay, and no person knew of the birth of the child. It was not welcome when it came, and as soon as it was born it died. Then the mother carried it at dead of night, along the narrow path over the rocks, past where the waters of Gob-yn-Ushtey leap into the bay, past Ooig-ny-Goayr, the Cave of the Goat, to Lag-ny-Killey. She buried it in the ruins of the lonely little Keeill that has been there on the hill-side for fourteen hundred years and more. There she left it alone.

A short while after some yawls were going to the haddock fishing from Dalby. There was the 'Lucky Granny' from the Lagg, the Muck Beg, or Little Pig, from Cubbon Aalish's, Boid-y-Conney from Cleary's, Glen Rushen, and others, ten in all. Then it began to be said that something strange was going on over at Lag-ny-Killey. The men would be fishing close in to land under the black shadow of Cronk-yn-Irree-Laa, the Hill of the Rising Day. When little evening came, the yawls would be drifting south with the flood tide, north with the ebb, passing and re-passing the strand of Lag-ny-Killey. Then they would see a beautiful light and hear a lamentation and crying, as if from a little lost child. In the end the light would run up the steep brow to the old Keeill, and go out. The men got so frightened that at last they would not go on the bay after dark, but would make from the fishing-ground as soon as the sun was getting low.

Things became so black for the women and children at home that one old, old man, Illiam Quirk, who had not gone to sea for many years, said he would go with one of the yawls to see for himself. They used to say of him: 'Oul Illiam has the power at him in the prayer, and he is a middlin' despard fella; he will dar' most anything.' It was so at this time—his yawl was the last of them coming in; the rest were frightened. It was a right fine, beautiful moonlight night when he was coming down from the mark, and when he was near to Gob-yn-Ushtey he heard crying and crying. He lay on his oars and listened, and he heard a little child wailing over and over again: 'She lhiannoo beg dyn ennym mee!' That is, 'I am a little child without a name!'

'Pull nearer to the lan',' said Illiam when he heard it. They pulled close in, and he plainly saw a little child on the strand bearing a lighted candle in its hand.

'God bless me, bogh, we mus' give thee a name!' said Illiam. And he took off his hat, and stood up in the boat, and threw a handful of water towards the child, crying out: 'If thou are a boy, I chrizzen thee in the name of the Father, Son, and Holy Ghost, Juan! If thou are a girl I chrizzen thee in the name of the Father, Son, and Holy Ghost, Joanney!'

In an instant the crying stopped, and was never heard again, and the light went out and was seen no more.

THE shoemakers and tailors and chance spinners used to go round on people's houses, making things and spinning rolls of wool for the people.

One time the tailor went to Chalse Ballawhane. Long enough they were waiting for him, and, as luck happened, he caught Chalse at home.

Now Chalse had power over the fishes of the sea and the birds of the air as well as over the beasts of the field. Himself and the Little Ones got on well together too, but somehow or other he was never able to get the power over them. People said he was never able to learn their language right. Anyhow, be that as it may, he was often enough with them.

After the tailor had had a crack with the women he turned round to Ballawhane, who was sitting in the big chair, his elbow on the table and his hand holding his forehead, the other hand in his trouser's pocket up to the elbow, and he not minding anybody nor anything.

'I batter take yer measure, Mr. Teare, while yer in, for there's no knowin' how long that'll be,' the tailor said.

'Aw, boy, boy,' answered Chalse, looking out through the window—people were not bothering with blinds then—and then turning to the clock, he said: There's no time goin' to-night: I want to go from home apiece, an' it's time I was gettin' ready.' Nobody said a word for a minute or two. He was exactly like a body with his mind far away. Again, all of a sudden, he looked at the tailor. Then he said:

'Ahm goin' to a big supper to-night.

Thou'll get nothin' done here, maybe thou would like to go? It's apiece to go, but thou'll be right enough with me. But there's one promise I'll be wantin' from thee—no matter, no matter what thou'll see, nor what thou'll hear, nor who'll spake to thee, thou mustn't spake back, or it'll be all over with thee.'

The tailor was so taken up with the chance of seeing the Little People for himself that he promised faithfully, no matter what took place, never to speak a word, and he knew he would be right enough with Chalse.

Ballawhane then took his hat from the *latt*, and when he was going out he said:

'I'll be back for thee just now; side thee things a bit while thou're waitin'.'

In a while there was a noise of horses coming up the street—it was awful. Then they stopped on the street and in came Ballawhane saying:

'We couldn' get another hoss for thee, boy, do what we would, but thou'll have to get a hoss of some sort.'

And going down to the parlour he got hold of something, and went out, never saying a word. Coming back to the door after a bit, he said:

'Come on, boy. I'll hold her head till thou get on.'

Out goes the tailor, and up, with one whip, on her back, and they go like the very hommers, on and on, over hedges and ditches, till they came to a big brow by a river. It seems they knew the way, night as it was, for they all took it one after another like fun. It was a big jump, though, and when the tailor felt himself flying through the air, his heart jumped to his mouth.

'Oh Lord, what a jump!' he said.

The next minute he fell flop in a bog, with the lapboard between his legs, all alone in the dark. Next morning he got up all slaaed with slush, looking like a thing that had been dragged through a gutter, and as quiet as a mouse—the shy he was, every bit of steam took out of him.

Awhile after some of the women were

asking him, how did he like it last night, and would he go again? But all they could get out of him was:

'Aw, navar no more, navar no more!'

JOE MOORE'S STORY OF FINN MAC-COOILL AND THE BUGGANE

Finn MacCooill was an Irish giant, and the Buggane was a Manx giant. But, anyway at all, this Finn came across from the Mountains of Mourne to see what was the Isle of Mann like, for he was seeing land. He liked the island uncommon well, so he stopped in it, living out Cregneish way. The Buggane was hearing great talk about the giant Finn MacCooill that was in the Sound, so he came down from the top of Barrule to put a sight on him. Finn knew that he was coming to have a fight with him, to see who was best man, and Finn did not want to fight. 'Lave him to me,' says the wife; 'an' I'll put the augh-augh on him!'

Before long they caught sight of the Buggane, and he was a walking terror. He was coming from Barrule to them, in a mighty pursue.

'Slip in the criddle, Finn,' says she. 'It's me that'll spake to him.'

Up comes the Buggane to the door, hot-foot.

'Where's Himself?' says he.

'This man is gone from home this bit,' says she. 'What is it you are wantin' with him?'

'Aw, there is no hurry on me. I'll put my fut inside and wait till he comes back,' says he.

'Plaze yourself,' says she, 'an' you'll plaze me; but I must get on with my bakin'.'

'Who have you got in the criddle?' says he.

'That's our baby,' says she.

'An' in the name of the Unknown

Powers, what sort of a man is he Himself if his baby is that big?'

'He's very big an' powerful,' says she. 'An' the child is favourin' the father.'

She was baking barley bread, and when the baking was done at her, she took the griddle and put it between two cakes of bread, and gave it to the Buggane to eat. with a quart of buttermilk. He went to try and eat, and he couldn'.

'Aw, man alive! But this is the hard bread,' says he. 'What sort have you given me at all, at all?'

'That's the sort I'm giving Finn,' says she.

'An' will Finn's teeth go through this?'

'Aw, yes, Finn thought nothing at all of 'ating that—that's the sort of bread he was wantin',' says Thrinn.

Finn got up out of the cradle, and began to roar for a piece. She fetched him a clout on the lug.

'Stop your noisin',' says she, 'An' stand straight and don't be puttin' the drone on yer back like that.' And givin' him a butter-cake, she says:

'Ate, ate, lash into ye, an' let's have no lavins.'

'You'll have the chile's teeth broke in his head, woman. He can navar ate bread as hard as that!' says the Buggane.

'Aw, he can do that with life,' says she.

But that done the Buggane; he sleeched out and claned away again. He thought if Finn was that strong and the baby that big, he had better catch home again.

But it was not long until the Buggane and Finn did meet, and then they had the battle! One day Finn met the Buggane over at Kirk Christ Rushen, and they went at each other early in the day till the sunset. Finn had one fut in the Big Sound, an' so he made the Channel between the Calf and Kitterland, and the other in the Little Sound, an' so he made the narrow Channel between Kitterland and the islan'. The Buggane was standin' at Port Iern—that's what made the fine big openin' at Port Iern. The rocks were all broken to pieces with their feet. But, anyway, the Buggane came off victorious and slashed Finn awful, so he had to run to Ireland. Finn could walk on the sea, but the Buggane couldn'; and when Finn got off and he couldn' get more revenge on him, he tore out a tooth and hove it whizzing through the air after Finn. It hit him on the back of the head, and then it fell into the sea and became what we are now calling the Chickens' Rock. Finn turned round with a roar and a mighty curse:

'My seven swearings of a curse on it!' says he. 'Let it lie there for a vexation to the sons of men while water runs and grass grows!'

And a vexation and a curse has it been to seamen from that day to this.

The Fynoderee went to the meadow
To lift the dew at grey cock crow,
The maiden hair and the cow herb
He was stamping them both his feet under;
He was stretching himself on the meadow,
He threw the grass on the left hand;
Last year he caused us to wonder,
This year he's doing far better.

He was stretching himself on the meadow,
The herbs in bloom he was cutting,
The bog bean herb in the curragh,
As he went on his way it was shaking,
Everything with his scythe he was cutting,
To sods was skinning the meadows,
And if a leaf were left standing,
With his heels he was stamping it under.

Old Song.

THE FYNODEREE OF GORDON

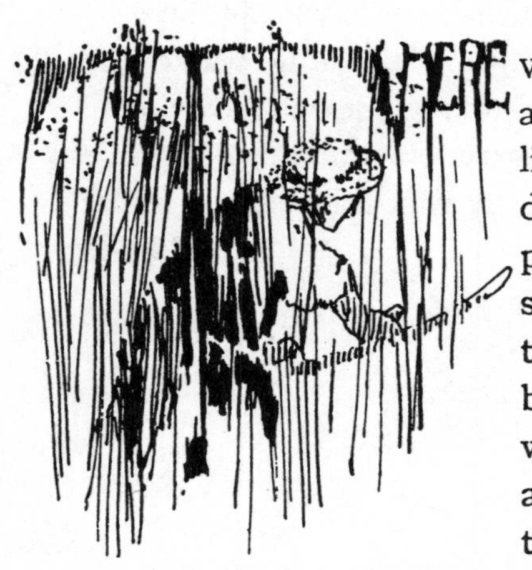

WAS one time a Fynoderee living in Gordon. Those persons who saw him said that he was big and shaggy with fiery eyes, and stronger than any man. One night he met the blacksmith who was going home from his shop and held out his hand to him to shake hands. The blacksmith gave him hold of the iron sock of the plough which he had with him, and he squeezed it as if it had been a piece of clay, saying: 'There's some strong Manxmen in the world yet!'

The Fynoderee did all his work at night and went into hidlans in the daytime. One night, when he was out on his travels he came to Mullin Sayle, out in Glen Garragh. He saw a light in the mill, so he put his head through the open top-half of the door to see what was going on inside, and there was Quaye Mooar's wife sifting corn. When she caught sight of the great big head she was frightened terrible. She had presence of mind, however, to hand him the sieve and say: 'If thou go to the river and bring water in it, I'll make a cake for thee; and the more water thou carry back, that's the bigger thy cake will be.'

So the Fynoderee took the sieve, and ran down to the river; but the water poured from it and he could fetch none for the cake, and he threw the sieve away in a rage, and cried:

'Dollan, dollan, dash!	Sieve, sieve, dash!
Ny smoo ta mee cur ayn,	The more I put in
Ny smoo ta goll ass.'	The more there's going out.

The woman got away while he was trying to fill the sieve, and when he came back to the mill he found it in darkness.

The Fynoderee was working very hard for the Radcliffes, who owned Gordon then. Every night he was grinding their corn for them, and often he would take a hand at the flails. If they put a stack into the barn in the evening and loosed every sheaf of it, they would find it thrashed in the morning, but he would not touch one sheaf of it unless it were loosed. In the summer time he was getting in their hay and cutting their corn.

Many a time the people of the farm were passing the time of day with him. One cold frosty day, big Gordon was docking turnips and he blew on his fingers to warm them.

'What are thou blowing on thee fingers for?' said the Fynoderee.

'To put them in heat,' said the Farmer.

At supper that night the Farmer's porridge was hot and he blew on it.

'What are thou doing that for?' said the Fynoderee. 'Isn't it hot enough for thee?'

'It's too hot, it is; I'm blowing on it to cool it,' said the Farmer.

'I don't like thee at all, boy,' said the Fynoderee, 'for thou can blow hot and blow cold with one breath.'

The Fynoderee was wearing no clothes, but it is said that he never felt the cold. Big Gordon, however, had pity on him that he had none, and one frosty winter he went and got clothes made for him—breeches, jacket, waistcoat and cap—great big ones they were too. And he went and gave them to him in the barn one night. The Fynoderee looked on them and took them up, and says he:

Coat for the back is sickness for the back!
Vest for the middle is bad for the middle!
Breeches for the breech is a curse for the breech!
Cap for the head is injurious for the head!
If thou own big Gordon farm, boy—
If thine this little glen east, and thine this little glen west,
Not thine the merry Glen of Rushen yet, boy!

So he flung the clothes away and walked his ways to Glen Rushen, out to Juan Mooar Cleary's. He was working for him then, cutting the meadow hay for him, cutting turf for him, and seeing after the sheep.

It happened one winter's night that there was a great snow-storm. Juan Mooar got up to see after the sheep, but the Fynoderee came to the window.

'Lie, lie an' take a sleep, Juan,' says he; 'I've got all the sheep in the fold, but there was one loaghtan (brown native sheep) yearling there that give me more trouble till all the res'. My seven curses on the little loaghtan! I was twice round Barrule Mooar afther her, but I caught her for all.'

When Juan went out in the morning all the sheep were safe in the cogee house and a big hare in with them, with two short lankets on him, that was the brown yearling!

After a time the Fynoderee went up to the top of Barrule Mountain to live, up to the very peak. Himself and the wife went to make a potful of porridge one day, and they fell out.

She ran and left him. He threw a big white rock after her and it struck her on the heel—the mark of the blood is still on the stone at Cleigh Fainey. While she stooped to put a rag on her heel he threw a lot of small rocks at her, that made her give a spring to the Lagg, two miles away. Then he threw a big rock with the pot-stick in it—it's in the Lagg river to-day. At that she gave two leaps over the sea to the Mountains of Mourne in Ireland; and for all that I know she's living there still.

THE LHONDOO AND THE USHAG-REAISHT

time Lhondoo, the Blackbird, was living in the mountains and Ushag-reaisht, the Bird of the Waste, as Manx ones call the Golden Plover, was living in the low-lands, and neither of them was able to leave his own haunts. One day, however, the two birds met on the borders between mountain and plain, and they made it up between them that they would change places for awhile. The Bird of the Waste should stay in the mountains till the Lhondoo should return.

The Lhondoo found himself better off in his new home than in the old one and he did not go back. So the poor Bird of the Waste was left in the mountains and any day you may hear him cry in a mournful voice:

> 'Lhondoo, vel oo cheet, vel oo cheet ?
> S'foddey my reayllagh oo!
> Black Thrush, are you coming, are you coming?
> The time is long and you are not here!

But the Lhondoo answers:

> 'Cha jig dy braa, cha jig dy braa!'
> Will never come, will never come!

Then the poor Ushag-reaisht wails:

> 'T'eh feer feayr, t'en feer feayr!'
> It's very cold, it's very cold.

Then the Blackbird goes his ways.

BILLY BEG, TOM BEG, AND THE FAIRIES

far from Dalby, Billy Beg and Tom Beg, two humpback cobblers, lived together on a lonely croft. Billy Beg was sharper and cleverer than Tom Beg, who was always at his command. One day Billy Beg gave Tom a staff, and quoth he:

'Tom Beg, go to the mountain and fetch home the white sheep.'

Tom Beg took the staff and went to the mountain, but he could not find the white sheep. At last, when he was far from home and dusk was coming on, he began to think that he had best go back. The night was fine, and stars and a small crescent moon were in the sky. No sound was to be heard but the curlew's sharp whistle. Tom was hastening home, and had almost reached Glen Rushen, when a grey mist gathered and he lost his way. But it was not long before the mist cleared, and Tom Beg found himself in a green glen such as he had never seen before, though he thought he knew every glen within five miles of him, for he was born and reared in the neighbourhood. He was marvelling and wondering where he could be, when he heard a far-away sound drawing nearer to him.

'Aw,' said he to himself, 'there's more than myself afoot on the mountains to-night; I'll have company.'

The sound grew louder. First, it was like the humming of bees, then like the rushing of Glen Meay waterfall, and last it was like the marching and the murmur of a crowd. It was the fairy host. Of a sudden the glen was full of fine horses and of Little People riding on them, with the lights on their red caps, shining like the stars above, and making the night as bright as day. There was the blowing of horns, and the waving of flags, the playing of music, and the barking of many little dogs. Tom Beg thought that he had never seen anything so splendid as all he saw there. In the midst of the drilling and dancing and singing one of them spied Tom, and then Tom saw coming towards him the grandest Little Man he had ever set eyes upon, dressed in gold and silver, and silk shining like a raven's wing.

'It is a bad time you have chosen to come this way,' said the Little Man, who was the king.

'Yes; but it is not here that I'm wishing to be though,' said Tom.

Then said the king: 'Are you one of us to-night, Tom?'

'I am surely,' said Tom.

'Then,' said the king, 'it will be your duty to take the password. You must stand at the foot of the glen, and as each regiment goes by, you must take the password: it is Monday, Tuesday, Wednesday, Thursday, Friday, Saturday.'

'I'll do that with a heart and a half,' said Tom.

At daybreak the fiddlers took up their fiddles, the Fairy army set itself in order, the fiddlers played before them out of the glen, and sweet that music was. Each regiment gave the password to Tom as it went by—Monday, Tuesday, Wednesday, Thursday, Friday, Saturday; and last of all came the king, and he, too, gave it—Monday, Tuesday, Wednesday, Thursday, Friday, Saturday. Then he called in Manx to one of his men:

'Take the hump from this fellow's back,' and before the words were out of his mouth the hump was whisked off Tom Beg's back and thrown into the hedge. How proud now was Tom, who so found himself the straightest man in the Isle of Mann! He went down the mountain and came home early in the morning with light heart and eager step. Billy Beg wondered greatly when he saw Tom Beg so straight and strong, and when Tom Beg had rested and refreshed himself he told his story:

how he had met the Fairies who came every night to Glen Rushen to drill.

The next night Billy Beg set off along the mountain road and came at last to the green glen. About midnight he heard the trampling of horses, the lashing of whips, the barking of dogs, and a great hullabaloo, and, behold, the Fairies and their king, their dogs and their horses, all at drill in the glen as Tom Beg had said.

When they saw the humpback they all stopped, and one came forward and very crossly asked his business.

'I am one of Yourselves for the night, and should be glad to do you some service,' said Billy Beg.

So he was set to take the password—Monday, Tuesday, Wednesday, Thursday, Friday, Saturday. And at daybreak the King said: 'It's time for us to be off,' and up came regiment after regiment giving Billy Beg the password—Monday, Tuesday, Wednesday, Thursday, Friday, Saturday. Last of all came the king with his men, and gave the password also—Monday,

Tuesday, Wednesday, Thursday, Friday, Saturday, 'AND SUNDAY,' says Billy Beg, thinking himself clever. Then there was a great outcry.

'Get the hump that was taken off that fellow's back last night and put it on this man's back,' said the King, with flashing eyes, pointing to the hump that lay under the hedge.

Before the words were well out of his mouth the hump was clapt on to Billy Beg's back.

'Now,' said the King, 'be off, and if ever I find you here again, I will clap another hump on to your front!'

And on that they all marched away with one great shout, and left poor Billy Beg standing where they had found him, with a hump growing on each shoulder. And he came home next day dragging one foot after another, with a wizened face and as cross as two sticks, with his two humps on his back, and if they are not off they are there still.

WELL,

there was a woman once, and she was scandalous lazy. She was that lazy she would do nothing but sit in the corner of the *chiollagh* warming herself, or going on the houses for newses the day long. And one day her man gives her some wool to spin for him ; he was terrible badly off for clothes to wear, for she was letting them get all ragged on him. He had told her to mend them until he was tired, but all he could get out of her was '*Traa dy liooar*' Time enough !

One day he comes to her, and says: 'Thou *lhiggey myr hraa*, here is some wool for thee to spin, and if it is not done a month from this day, I 'll throw thee out on the side of the road. Thou and thy *Traa dy liooar* have left me nearly bare.'

Well, she was too lazy to spin, but she would be pretending to be working hard when the husband was in the house. She used to put the wheel out on the floor every night before the husband came in from work, to let on to him that she had been spinning.

The husband was asking her was the thread getting near spun, for he said he was seeing the wheel so often on the floor that he wanted to know if she had enough to take to the weaver. When it came to the last week but one, she had only one ball spun, and that one was knotted and as coarse as gorse. When her husband says to her:

'I'm seeing the wheel middling often on the floor when I come home at night; may-be there 's enough thread spun at thee now for me to take to the weaver next week?'

'I don't know, at all,' says the wife. 'Maybe there is; let us count the balls.'

Then the play began! Up she went on the *lout*, and flung the ball through the hole, down to him.

'Keep count thyself, and fling the balls back again to me,' says she to the man. And as fast as he flung the ball up to her, so fast she flung it down to him again. When he had counted the ball, maybe, two score times, she says to him:

'That's all that's in.'

'Aw, 'deed, you've spun well, woman, for all,' says he; 'there's plenty done at thee for the weaver.'

Aw, then she was in a great fix, and didn't know in her senses what to do to save herself. She knew she would sup sorrow if she was found out, but she could think of nothing.

At last she bethought herself of the Giant that lived in a lonesome place up the mountain, for she had heard tell he was good to work, and the woman, she says to herself:

'I've a mind to go my ways to him.' She took the road early next morning, she and her rolls of wool, and she walked up hills, down gills, till at last she came to the Giant's house.

'What are thou wanting here?' says the Giant.

'I'm wanting thee to help me,' says she: and she up and told him about the ball of thread and everything.

'I'll spin the wool for thee,' says the Giant, 'if thou'll tell me my name when thou come for the balls a week from this day. Are thou satisfied?'

'Why shouldn't I be satisfied?' says the woman; for she thought to herself it would be a middling queer thing if she couldn't find out his name within a week. Well, the woman she tried every way to find out the Giant's name, but, go where she might, no one had ever heard tell of it. The time was getting over fast, and she was no nearer to the Giant's name. At last it came to the last day but one.

Now, as it happened, the husband was

coming home from the mountain that day in the little evening, and as he neared the Giant's house, he saw it all in a blaze of light, and there was a great whirling and whistling coming to his ears, and along with it came singing, and laughing, and shouting. So he drew near the window, and then he sees the big Giant inside sitting at a wheel, spinning like the wind, and his hands flying with the thread to and fro, to and fro, like the lightning, and he shouting to the whistling wheel: 'Spin, wheel, spin faster; and sing, wheel, sing louder!'

And he sings, as the wheel whirls faster and faster:

'Snieu, queeyl, snieu; 'rane, queeyl, 'rane;
Dy chooilley clea er y thie, snieu er my skyn.
Lheeish yn ollan, lhiams y snaie,
S'beg fys t'ec yn ven litcheragh
Dy re Mollyndroat my ennym!'

Spin, wheel, spin; sing, wheel, sing;
Every beam on the house, spin overhead.
Herself's is the wool, mine is the thread,
How little she knows, the lazy wife,
That my name is Mollyndroat!

When the husband got home that evening he was late, and his wife said to him :

'Where have you been so late? Did thou hear anything new?'

Then he said:

'Thou are middling good to spin thyself, *ven thie*; but I'm thinking there's one in that's better than thee, for all. Never in all my born days did I see such spinning, a thread as fine as a cobweb, and hear such singing as there was going on in the Giant's house to-night.'

'What was he singing?' says the wife. And he sang the song to her :

Snieu, queeyl, snieu; 'rane, queeyl, 'rane;
Dy chooilley clea er y thie, snieu er my skyn.
Lheeish yn ollan, lhiams y snaie,
S'beg fys t'ec yn ven litcheragh
Dy re Mollyndroat my ennym!

Well, well, the joy the woman took when she heard the song!

'Aw, what sweet music! Sing it again, my good man,' says she.

And he sang it to her again, till she knew it by heart.

Early next morning, she went as fast as her feet could carry her to the Giant's house. The road was long, and a bit lonesome under the trees, and to keep up her heart she sang to herself:

> Snieu, queeyl, snieu; snieu, queeyl, snieu;
> Dy chooilley vangan er y villey, snieu er my skyn
> S'lesh hene yn ollan, as lhiam pene y snaie,
> Son shenn Mollyndroat cha vow eh dy braa.'
>
> Spin, wheel, spin; spin, wheel, spin;
> Every branch on the tree, spin overhead.
> The wool is Himself's, the thread is my own,
> For old Mollyndroat will never get it.

When she got to the house, she found the door open before her, and in she went.

'I've come again for the thread,' says she.

'Aisy, aisy, good woman,' says the Giant. 'If thou don't tell me my name thou won't get the thread—that was the bargain.' And says he: 'Now, what's my name?'

'Is it Mollyrea?' says she—to let on that she didn't know it.

'No, it is not,' says he.

'Are you one of the Mollyruiy ones?' says she.

'I'm not one of that clan,' says he.

'Are they calling you Mollyvridey?' says she.

'They are not,' says he.

'I'll warrant your name is Mollychreest?' says she.

'You are wrong, though,' says he.

'Are you going by the name of Molly-voirrey?' says she.

''Deed I am not,' says he.

'Maybe your name is Mollyvartin?' says she.

'And, maybe, it's not at all,' says he.

'They're saying,' says she, 'that there was only seven families living on the islan' at one time, and their names all began with "Molly"; and so,' says she, 'if you are not a Mollycharaine, you are none of the rael, oul' Manx ones, at all.'

'I am not a Mollycharaine,' says he. 'Now, be careful, woman; next guess is your last.'

At that she pretended to be frightened, and says she, slowly, pointing her finger at him:

'S'lesh hene yn ollan, as lhiam pene y snaie,
Son shenn—Moll-YN-DROAT cha vow eh dy braa.'
The wool is Himself's, and the thread is my own,
For old—Moll-YN-DROAT will never get it.

Well the Giant, he was done, and he was in a red rage, and he cries :

'Bad luck to you ! You never would have found out my name unless you're a *mummig yn aishnee.*'

'Bad luck to yourself, my boy,' says she, 'for trying to steal a dacent woman's wool.'

'Go to the Devil, yourself and your fortune-telling,' shouts he, jumping up and flinging the balls at her.

And away home with her, and her balls of thread. And if she didn't spin her own wool for ever after, that's nothing to do with you and me.

THE MERMAID OF GOB NY OOYL

ONCE on a time there lived at the bottom end of Cornah gill a family of the name of Sayle, and the Mermaid who had her haunt up Bulgham way was a friend to them. They were always in luck's way and never seemed to be short of anything. Sure enough they were full of thrift, and to fill in odds of spare time they made lobster pots from the osier that grew around in plenty, and they always found a ready market. They kept a cow and a few sheep, just to give work to the women in the long winter nights, but their living was mostly got by the sea.

It was well known that Sayle had a strong liking for apples, and that he would often bring some with him out in the boat, but when he got well up in years he would be leaving a lot of the boat-work for the boys, and then the luck began to get less, and many a time one of them had to take a gun to keep something in the pot. Then the bigger ones took to the herrings. One, Evan, however, had to stay about to keep things going, and it happened that one day, after he had the creels set, just at Bulgham, that he pulled the boat in and went up the brow after eggs. On coming back to the boat he heard some one calling to him, and, looking round, he saw a fine-looking woman sitting on the edge of a rock.

'And how's your father?' said she. 'It's seldom he's coming this way now.'

Young Sayle was a bit frightened at first, but seeing a pleasant look on her face, he took courage and told her how things were at home. Then saying she hoped to see him again, she slipped into the water and disappeared.

On getting home he told what had taken place, and the father, his face lighting up, declared:

'There will be luck on the house yet.'

And he said:

'Take some apples with you the next time you go up that way, an' we'll see.'

The very next time the young chap went, he took some apples with him, and when he got to the place where he had seen the beautiful woman, he went, as usual, on the hunt among the rocks. Then he heard sweet singing, and when he turned round what should he see but the Mermaid leaning over the boat and smiling pleasantly. She took an apple and began to eat and chant:

The luck o' the sea be with you, but don't forgetful be
Of bringing some sweet lan' eggs for the children of the sea.

From that time he was nearly living on the water until, at last, he was taken to task for being idle. Then he made up his mind to go sailing in foreign parts. The Mermaid was in great distress, so to please her, he went and planted an apple tree on the brow above her haunt, telling her that when he would be far away this tree would grow land-eggs which, when they would be sweet and ready for eating, would come of themselves to the water for her. And, sure enough, the luck of the family remained, though the boy was gone.

She seemed to bear up well for a long time and would often be seen sitting on the rocks in the evening, singing sad songs, and casting longing glances up to the apple tree above. She kept very shy of everyone coming her way, and at last, finding the apples slow in coming, made up her mind to go in search of young Sayle, hoping the apples would be ready for taking when they would come back.

But neither of them ever came back, though for many a long year the apple tree bore fruit and marked the little creek where the Mermaid used to live.

ONE time the Farmer of Ballaleece married a beautiful young wife and they were thinking the world of one another. But before long she disappeared. Some persons said that she was dead and others that she was taken by the Little People. Ballaleece mourned for her with a heavy heart and looked for her from Point of Ayr to the

Calf; but in the end, not finding her, he married another wife. This one was not beautiful, but there was some money at her.

Soon after the marriage his first wife appeared to Ballaleece one night, and said to him:

'My man, my man, I was taken away by the Little People, and I live with them near to you. I can be set free if you will but do what I tell you.'

'Tell me quick,' said Ballaleece.

'We'll be riding through Ballaleece barn at midnight on Friday,' said she. 'We'll be going in on one door and out on another. I'll be riding behind one of the men on horseback. You'll sweep the barn clean, and mind there is not one straw left on the floor. Catch hold of my bridle rein, hold it fast, and I shall be free.'

When the night came Ballaleece took a besom and swept the barn floor so clean that not one speck was left on it. Then he waited in the dark.

At midnight the barn doors opened wide,

sweet music was heard, and in through the open door came a fine company of Little People, in green jackets and red caps, riding fine horses. On the last horse, sitting behind a Little Fellow, Ballaleece saw his first wife as pretty as a picture, and as young as when she left him. He seized hold of her bridle rein, but he was shaken from side to side like a leaf on a tree, and he was not able to hold her. As she went out through the door she stretched out her right hand and pointed to a bushel in the corner of the barn, and called out in a sad voice :

'There's been a straw put under the bushel—for that reason you could'nt hold me, and you've done with me for ever ! '

The second wife had heard what had passed and had hidden the straw, and turned the bushel upside down so that it would not be seen.

The young wife was never heard of any more.

SMEREREE

THE speckled hen and the little chicken were scratching under an apple tree in the garden, and an apple fell off the tree and it hit the little chicken on the head. And says he to the speckled hen:

'Let us go to Rome, for the world has fallen.'

'Who said that to you, little chicken?' said the speckled hen.

'It fell on my head, Smereree!'

Then the speckled hen and the little chicken went their ways until they met the cock.

'Where are you going, speckled hen?' said the cock.

'Going to Rome, for the world has fallen,' said the speckled hen.

'Who said that to you, speckled hen?'

'The little chicken said it to me.'

'Who said that to you, little chicken?'

'It fell on my head, Smereree!'

So they went their ways together until they met a gander.

'Where are you going, cock?' said the gander.

'Going to Rome, for the world has fallen.'

'Who said that to you, cock?' said the gander.

'The speckled hen said it to me.'

'Who said that to you, speckled hen?'

'The little chicken said it to me.'

'Who said that to you, little chicken?'

'It fell on my head, Smereree!'

So they went all together until they met a bull.

'Where are you going, gander?' said the bull.

'Going to Rome, for the world has fallen.'

'Who said that to you, gander?'

'The cock said it to me.'

'Who said that to you, cock?'

'The speckled hen said it to me.'

'Who said that to you, speckled hen?'

'The little chicken said it to me.'

'Who said that to you, little chicken?'

'It fell on my head, Smereree!'

So they went all together until they met a goat.

'Where are you going, bull?' said the goat.

'Going to Rome, for the world has fallen,' said the bull.

'Who said that to you, bull?' said the goat.

'The gander said it to me.'

'Who said that to you, gander?'

'The cock said it to me.'

'Who said that to you, cock?'

'The speckled hen said it to me.'

'Who said that to you, speckled hen?'

'The little chicken said it to me.'

'Who said that to you, little chicken?'

'It fell on my head, Smereree!'

So they all went together until they met a horse.

'Where are you going, goat?' said the horse.

'Going to Rome, for the world has fallen.'

'Who said that to you, goat?'
'The bull said it to me.'
'Who said that to you, bull?'
'The gander said it to me.'
'Who said that to you, gander?'
'The cock said it to me.'
'Who said that to you, cock?'
'The speckled hen said it to me.'
'Who said that to you, speckled hen?'
'The little chicken said it to me.'
'Who said that to you, little chicken?'
'It fell on my head, Smereree!'

So they all went travelling together until they came to the house of the giant; they went in the house and the giant was from home. So the horse went under the big table, and the bull went under the dresser, and the goat went on the stairs, and all the rest in the corners.

When the giant came home, they all went at him at once, and there was heavy war between them.

'Calk! Calk! If I come down to you,' said the cock.

He came down at last and picked the

giant's eyes out, and they killed him, and they all lived in his house together.

And if they are not dead, they are living there yet.

KEBEG

HERE is a deep dub, or pool, on Ballacoan stream, which the children of Laxey call Nikkesen's. It is the home of Nyker, the Water Goblin. It has no bottom; and brambles and ferns are growing round it, and fir trees and hazels are hiding it from sight. No child, no grown-up person even, will go near it after dark.

A great many years ago a beautiful girl living at Ballaquine was sent to look for the calves, which had gone astray. She had got as far as Nikkesen's, when she took a notion that she heard the calves over the river in Johnny Baldoon's nuts. At once she began to call to them :

'Kebeg ! Kebeg ! Kebeg !'

so loud that you could hear her at Chibber

Pherick, Patrick's Well. The people could hear her calling quite plainly, but, behold, a great mist came and rolled down the valley, and shut it from sight. The people on one side of the valley could hear her voice yet calling through the mist:

'Kebeg! Kebeg! Kebeg!'

Then came a little sweet voice through the mist and the trees in answer:

'Kebeg's here! Kebeg's here!'

And she cried:

'I'm comin'! I'm comin'!'

And that was all.

The Fairies who live in Nikkesen's had pulled her in, and carried her to their own home.

She was never heard of again.

THE FAIRY CHILD OF CLOSE NY LHEIY

NE time there was a woman named Colloo, in Close ny Lheiy, near Glen Meay, and she had a child that had fallen sick in a strange way. Nothing seemed wrong with him, yet crosser and crosser he grew, *nying nyanging* night and day. The woman was in great distress. Charms had failed, and she didn't know rightly what to do.

It seems that when about a fortnight old, the child, as fine a child for his age as you would see in a day's walk, was left asleep while the mother went to the well for water. Now Herself forgot to put the tongs on the cradle, and when she came back the child was crying pitifully, and there was no quieting for him. And from that very hour the flesh seemed to melt off his bones till he became as ugly and as wizened a child as you would see between the Point of Ayr and the Calf. He was that way, his whining howl filling the house, for four years, lying in his cradle without a motion on him to put his feet under him. Not a day's rest nor a night's sleep had the woman these four years with him. She was fairly scourged until there came a fine day in the spring, while Hom Beg Bridson, the tailor, was in the house sewing. Hom is dead now, but there's many alive that remember him yet. He was wise tremendous, for he was going from house to house sewing, and gathering wisdom as he was going.

Well, before that day the tailor was seeing lots of wickedness in the child. When the woman would be out feeding the cows and pigs, he would be hoisting his head up out of the cradle and making faces at the tailor, winking and slicking, and shaking his head, and saying 'What a lad I am!'

That day the woman wanted to go to the shop to sell some eggs that she had, and says she to the tailor: 'Hom, man, keep your eye on the chile that the bogh won't fall out of the criddle an' hurt himself, while I slip down to the shop.'

When she was gone the tailor began to whistle, low and slow, to himself, as he stitched, the tune of a little hymn.

'Drop that, Hom Beg,' said a little harsh voice.

The tailor, scandalised, looked round to see if it was the child that had spoken, and it was.

'Whush, whush, now; lie quate,' said the tailor, rocking the cradle with his foot, and as he rocked he whistled the hymn tune louder.

'Drop that, Hom Beg, I tell ye, an' give us something light an' handy,' said the little fella back to him, middling sharp.

'Aw, anything at all to plaze thee,' said the tailor, whistling a jig.

'Hom,' said my lad, 'can thou dance anything to that?'

'I can,' said the tailor. 'Can thou?'

'I can that,' said my lad. 'Would thou like to see me dance?'

'I would,' said the tailor.

'Take that oul' fiddle down, then, Hom, man,' he said; 'an' put "The tune of the Big Wheel" on it.'

'Aw, I'll do that for thee, an' welcome,' said the tailor.

The fiddle quits its hook on the wall, and the tailor tunes up.

'Hom,' said the little fella, 'before thou begin to play, clear the kitchen for me—cheers an' stools, everything away—make a place for me to step out to the music, man.'

'Aw, I'll do that for thee, too,' said the tailor. He cleared the kitchen floor, and then he struck up 'Tune y wheeyl vooar.'

In a crack the little fella bounced from his cradle on to the floor with a 'Chu!' and began flying round the kitchen.

'Go it, Hom—face your partner—heel an' toe does it. Well done, Hom—more power to your elba, man.'

Hom plays faster and faster, till my lad was jumping as high as the table. With a 'Chu!' up goes his foot on top of the dresser, and 'Chu!' then on top of the chimney piece, and 'Chu!' bang against the partition ; then he was half flying, half footing it round the kitchen, turning and going that quick that it put a reel in Hom's head to be looking at him. Then he was whirling everything round for a clear space, even Hom himself, who by degrees gets up on the table in the corner, and plays wilder and faster, as the whirling jig grows madder and swifter.

'M 'Yee ! ' said the tailor, throwing down the fiddle. 'I mus' run, thou 're not the chile that was in the criddle ! Are thou ? '

'Houl', man ! thou're right enough,' said the little fella. 'Strike up for me — make has'e, make has'e, man—keep joggin' your elba.'

'Whush ! ' said the tailor, 'here's Herself comin'.'

The dance suddenly ceased. The child gave a hop, skip, and jump into the cradle.

'Go on with thy sewing, Hom ; don't say a word,' said the little fella, covering himself up in the clothes till nothing was left of him to be seen except his eyes, which keeked out like a ferret's.

When Herself came in the house, the tailor, all of a tremble, was sitting cross-legged on the round table and his spec's on his nose and letting on that he was busy sewing; the child in the cradle was grinning and crying as usual.

'What in all the earthly worl'——! But it's the quare stitching, altogether, there's been goin' on here, and me out. An' how thou can see the needle in that dark corner, Hom Bridson, let alone sew, it bates me, said she, siding the place. 'Well, well—then, well, well—on the boghee millish. What is it at all, at all, that's doin' on the veen? Did he think Mammy had gone an' left him then, the chree? Mammy is goin' to feed him, though.'

The tailor had been thinking mighty with himself what he ought to do, so he said:

'Look here, woman, give him nothing at all, but go out an' get a creelful of good turf an' a whisp of feern.'

She brought the turf, and throws a bundle of fern on it.

The tailor gave a leap off the table down to the floor, and it wasn't long till he had the fine fire.

'Thou'll have the house put on fire for me, Hom,' said Herself.

'No fear, but I'll fire some of them,' said the tailor. The child, with his two eyes going out of his head watching to see what the tailor was going to do, was slowly turning his whining howl into a kind of call—to his own sort to come and fetch him, it's like.

'I'll send thee home,' said the tailor, drawing near the cradle, and he stretches out his two hands to take the child and put him on the big, red turf fire.

Before he was able to lay a hand on him, the little fella leaped out of the cradle and took for the door.

'The back of me han' an' the sole of me fut to you!' said he, 'if I would only a-had another night I could have showed thee a trick or two more than that yet.'

Then the door flew open with a bang, as though some one had thrown it open, and he took off with himself like a shot. A hullabaloo of laughing and making fun was heard outside, and the noise of many running little feet. Out of the door of the house goes Herself, and Hom after her; they see no one, but they caught sight of a flock of low-lying clouds shaped like gulls chasing each other away up Glen Rushen, and then came to their ears, as if afar off from the clouds, sharp whistles and wicked little laughs as if making mock of them. Then as they were turning round to come back, she suddenly sees right before her, her own sweet, rosy, smiling child, with thumb in mouth, lying on a mossy bank. And she took all the joy in the world of the child that he was back again safe and sound.

THE LITTLE FOOTPRINTS

CLOSE to the Niarbyl, the great tail of rock that stretches into the sea at Dalby, is a little house on the strand. It is sheltered behind by the high rock which rises above its thatched roof. Before it lies Baie Mooar, the great bay, held by a chain of mountains purple with ling. Standing before its door and looking to the west, you may see the sun set behind the distant Mourne Mountains. At dawn you may see her rise over Cronk-yn-Irree-Laa, the Hill of the Rising Day. Here lived Juan, the fisherman.

He knew, as well as any person, that the Little People were all around. When he was a boy he had many a time looked out of the door on moonlight nights to try if he could put a sight on them dancing on the lonely shore. He had not seen them —they make themselves invisible when they know that mortal eyes are on them. But he had seen the tiny riding lights of their herring fleet in the bay, and had helped his father to draw in the nets full of good fish, which were sure to be caught the night after. Many a time he had wakened from his sleep in the dark, and, in the pauses of the wind and the lull of the great breakers, he had heard the sound of hammering. He knew it was the Little People hammering at their herring barrels in Ooig-ny-Seyir, the Coopers' Cave, under the hills, and that as the chips flew out on to the waves they became ships.

He had heard the story of the fisherman, a friend of his father's, who was fishing one night at Lag-ny-Killey, when a dense grey mist rolled in. He thought he had best make for home while the footpath above the rocks was visible. When he was getting his things together he heard what sounded like a lot of children coming out of school.

He lifted his head, and, behold, there was a fleet of fairy boats each side of the rock, their riding lights shining like little stars on a frosty night. The crews seemed busy preparing to come on shore, and he heard one little fellow shout:

'Hraaghyn boght as earish broigh, skeddan dy liooar ec mooinjer yn theihll shoh, cha nel veg ain!'

Poor times and dirty weather, herring enough at the people of this world, nothing at us!

'Then,' said the fisherman, 'they dropped off and went agate o' the flitters.'

When Juan was a big boy he himself saw a thing which he never forgot. One day he left a boat over at the farther side of Baie Mooar, and at night he had to go over to fetch it. It was a moonlight night and the bay was as smooth as glass as he rowed across. There was no sound but the lapping of the little waves on the shore, and now and again the cry of a gannet. Juan found his boat on the strand where he had left her and was setting to work to launch her, when he thought he saw a glimmering light, which was not the light of the moon, in one of the caves near him. He stood where he was, and listened, and he heard the sound of faint music. Then he went as silently as he was able to the cave, and looked in. No light was there but the dim light of the moon. The shadows in the corners of the cave were as black as pitch.

Juan was trembling all over, and at first he was blinking his eyes and could see nothing. But after some minutes he saw a great stone in the midst of the cave and the floor of fine white sand. And on the sand around that stone there were little footprints—marks of tiny clogs they were, no bigger than his thumb!

TOM CRAINE was going home at midnight from Bradda mine to his home at Colby. The road was lonely and he met no person, but the full moon was shining and it was as light as day. As he began to pass under the trees that grow round the house at Ballacurry, a little dog appeared suddenly from the black shadow at the roadside and followed at his heels. He whistled to it, but as he turned his head to look at it, it ran on in front of him, and for a minute he did not see it. When he came in sight of it again, he was terrified to see that it had grown larger—as big as a goat—and it grew bigger and bigger till it was the size of a donkey ! It galloped before him and disappeared round the bend of the road where the gate of Ballacurry is. When Tom came to the gate he saw a very tall, thin man leaning on it, with his arms folded on the top of it. The beast was not there. As Tom reached the gate the tall thin man turned and walked up the long path that leads to the house. When he got to the door he turned again and walked back down the path towards Tom. By the bright moonlight Tom saw the lace ruffle round his neck, the satin of his knee breeches, the silk of his stockings, and the shining buckles on his shoes—the dress of bygone days. His face was white and dreadful. As Tom looked he was all at once taken with terror, and ran off as hard as he could go down the road to Colby.

He had not gone far when he met two of his friends, Ben Mylechreest and Bill Teare. He told them what he had seen, and they made fun of him and would not believe that he had seen any such thing. They said they would go back with him to the gate, so they all three turned back. When they got to the gate they saw the big man, as tall as two men, walking up the path with his back towards them. As before, when he reached the door, he turned—WHAT they saw they never told any man!

They took to their heels, all three; and ran till they could run no longer. They were trembling from head to foot and the sweat pouring out of them. They were too terrified to go home, so they turned in with Tom and they slept, all three, in one bed.

NED QUAYLE'S STORY OF THE FAIRY PIG

WHEN I was a little boy, we lived over by Sloc. One day, when I was six years old, my mother and my grandmother went up the mountain to make hay and I was left by myself. It was getting rather late, and they had not come back, so I was frightened, and started off up the mountain to try and find them. I had not gone far when I saw running before me a little snow-white pig. At first I thought it was some neighbour's pig, and I tried to catch it, but it ran from me and I ran after it. As it went I saw that it was not like an ordinary pig—its tail was feathery and spread out like a fan, and it had long lapping ears that swept the ling. Now and again it turned its head and looked at me, and its eyes were burning like fire. We went higher and higher up the mountain, and all of a sudden I found myself at the edge of a steep brow and was all but over. I turned just in time, and ran as hard as I could go down the mountain and the pig after me. When I looked back over my shoulder, I saw that it was jumping over the big stones and rocks on the mountain side as if they had been butts of ling. I thought it would catch me; it was close behind me when I ran in at our garden gate, but I was just in time, and I slammed the door upon it.

I told my mother and my grandmother what had happened, and my grandmother said it was a Fairy Pig. I was not like myself that night; I could not eat any supper, and I went soon to my bed; I could not sleep, but lay tossing about; and was burning hot. After a time my mother opened the door to see if I was asleep, and when she looked at me, HER EYES WERE LIKE THE PIG'S EYES. I felt a sharp pain go through my right leg like a stab. After that the pain never left me; it was so bad that I could not bear to be touched, and I could eat nothing. I grew worse and worse, and after some days my father said he would take me to a Charmer at Castletown. They lifted me in the sheet, four men taking the four corners, and carried me to a cart. Never will I forget the shaking and jolting I had in that cart. When we got to Castletown I was more dead than alive.

The Charmer lived in Arbory Street and they took me to his house. When he saw me he said that they must all go away and leave me alone with him, so my father and my mother went to wait for me at The George. The Charmer carried me to a room upstairs and sent his wife away, and laid me on the floor and locked the door. Then he took down a big book and placed it on the floor beside me. He opened it at the picture of a little plant—I can see the plant to this day—and he pointed with his left hand to the picture, and with his right hand he made the sign of the cross on my leg, where the stab went through me, and said:

'Ta mee skeaylley yn guin shoh ayns ennym yn Ayr, as y Vac, as y Spyrryd Noo, Ned Quayle. My she guin, ayns ennym y

Chiarn, ta mee skealley eh ass yn eill, ass ny fehyn, as ass ny craueyn,' which means in English— I spread this fairy shot in the name of the Father, and of the Son, and of the Holy Ghost, Ned Quayle. If it is a fairy shot, in the name of the Lord, I spread it out of the flesh, out of the sinews, and out of the bones. That minute the pain left me. I felt very hungry, and the Charmer's wife set me at a table and gave me dinner. The Charmer went to fetch my father and my mother, and when they came in I was eating like two.

The Charmer told my mother I must not go on the mountain alone between the lights again. The pain never came back. I have been sound from that day to this, but I have the mark on my leg where the stab went through as clear as glass to the bone.

SCENE :
A
VILLAGE

Blackbird
sings to
Innkeeper's
pretty
daughter.

kione jiarg

Apyrn doo, Apyrn doo,
Vel oo cheet ? Vel oo cheet ?
Skee fieau, skee fieau,
Lhondoo, Lhondoo.

Red head, red head,
Black apron, black apron,
Are you coming ? Are you coming ?
Tired waiting, tired waiting,
Blackbird, Blackbird.

IT WAS MORE than eight hundred years ago, in the days of Olaf Goddardson, that Baron Kitter, the Norwegian, lived in Mann. He had his castle on the top of Barrule, and he spent all his time in hunting the bisons and elks that were on the island then, until he had killed them all. Then the people began to be afraid that he would chase their cattle and the purrs of the mountains, and leave them no beasts at all, so they went to the wisest witches of the island, to see what they could do.

One day Baron Kitter had gone over to the Calf to hunt the red deer there, leaving his cook, Eaoch of the Loud Voice, in the castle to cook his dinner. Eaoch set the pot on the fire and then fell asleep over his work. While he was sleeping the witch-wife Ada put a spell on the pot, and the fat boiled over into the fire. Soon the house was in flames. Eaoch woke and shouted for help at the top of his voice, and his cries were so loud that they reached the ears of Kitter and his fellow-huntsmen, ten miles away on the Calf.

When Kitter heard the cries and saw the flames on the top of Barrule, he made for the beach as hard as he could, and put out in a small currach for the island, with most of his friends. When they were in the strong current about half-way across the channel, the boat struck on a rock and they were all drowned, and the rock has ever since been called Kitterland. The rest of Kitter's friends, who had stayed on the Calf and so saved their lives, believed that Eaoch, the cook, had made a plot with the witches of the island to do away with all the Norwegians in Mann, so they brought him before King Olaf to be judged, and he was condemned to death. But according to the custom of Norway, he was allowed to choose how he would die.

Then he said:

'I wish my head to be laid across one of your Majesty's legs, and there cut off by your Majesty's sword Macabuin, which was made by Loan Maclibuin, the Dark Smith of Drontheim!'

It was known to every person there that the king's sword could cut the hardest granite, only by touching it with its edge, and they all begged Olaf not to do as crafty Eaoch asked. But the king would not break his word and gave orders that all should be done as the cook had said.

But the witch Ada was there and she told them to take toads' skins, twigs of the cuirn tree, and adders' eggs, nine times nine of each, and put them between the king's leg and the cook's head. They did this, and then the great sword Macabuin, made by Loan Maclibuin, was lifted with the greatest care by one of the king's faithful servants and laid gently on the cook's neck, but before it could be stopped Eaoch's head was cut from his body and the adders' eggs and the cuirn twigs were also cut through— only the toads' skins saved the king's leg.

When the Dark Smith heard how the power of the great sword Macabuin had been stayed by witchcraft, he was very angry, and called for his Hammer-man, Hiallus-nan-urd, who had lost one leg when he was helping to make the sword. He sent him off at once to Peel Castle to challenge King Olaf, or any of his men, to a walking race from Peel to Drontheim. King Olaf himself took up the challenge, and off they set. Over mountains and through gills they walked, as fast as they could go, and the one-legged man as fast as the king. When they had crossed the island they each put out to sea in a sailing boat, and each came in sight of Drontheim at the same moment. When they drew near to the smithy, the Hammer-man, who was ahead, called out to Loan to open the door, and Olaf called to him to shut it, and then, pushing past Hiallus, got into the smithy first.

To show that he was not at all weary after his walk Olaf took up the great hammer of the forge and struck the anvil such a mighty blow that he split it through, and the block beneath it, too. When Emergaid, the daughter of Loan, saw the strength and power of Olaf, she loved him; and while her father was putting back the block and anvil, she whispered to the king:

'My Father is doing that, so that he may finish the sword he is making. It has been foretold that the first blood it shall shed shall be royal blood, and he has sworn that that blood shall be yours.'

'But is not your father the seventh son of Old Windy Cap, King of Norway?' cried Olaf.

'He is,' said Emergaid.

'Then the prophecy shall be fulfilled,' said Olaf, and he thrust the sword into the heart of Loan, and afterwards slew with it the Hammer-man also.

He made Emergaid his queen and they

ruled together, and from them came a long line of Kings of Mann.

TEEVAL, PRINCESS OF THE OCEAN

IN the old days Culain, the smith of the gods, was living in the Isle of Mann. It was the time when Conchubar was at the court of the King of Ulster, and had nothing but the sword in his hand. He was a fine handsome young man, and he had made up his mind to make himself a king. So he went one day to the Druid of Clogher to ask him what he had best do.

'Go thy way,' said the Druid, 'to the Isle of Mann. There thou wilt find the great smith Culain. Get him to make thee a sword and a spear and a shield, and with these thou shalt win the kingdom of Ulster.'

Conchubar went away and hired a boat and put out to sea. He landed in Mann and made straight for Culain's smithy. It was night when he got there, and the red glow of the furnace shone out into the dark. He could hear from inside the smithy the roar of the bellows and the clanging of the hammer on the anvil. When he came near, a great dog, as large as a calf, began to bay and to growl like thunder, and brought his master out.

'Who art thou, young man?' said he.

'Oh Culain!' cried Conchubar, 'It is from the Druid of Clogher that I come, and he bade me ask thee to make me a sword and a spear and a shield, for only with weapons of thy making can I win the Kingdom of Ulster.'

Culain's face grew black at first, but after he had gazed for a while at Conchubar, he saw that he had the look about him of one who would go far, and he said:

'It shall be done for thee, but thou must wait, for the work is long.'

So Culain began to make the weapons, and Conchubar waited in the island.

Early one brave morning in May when the sun had just risen over Cronk-yn-Irree-

Laa, he was walking on the strand wondering to himself how much longer Culain would be making his weapons and thinking it was full time for him to return. The tide was going out, and the sun was shining on the wet sand. Suddenly he saw something flashing at the edge of the waves a few paces from him. He ran up to it and, behold, it was the most beautiful woman he had ever put sight on, fast asleep. Her hair was golden like the gorse in bloom; her skin whiter than the foam of the sea, her lips red as the coral, and her cheeks rosy like the little clouds that were flying before the face of the rising sun. The fringe of her dress of many coloured seaweeds rose and fell with the ebb and flow of the waves. Pearls gleamed on her neck and arms. Conchubar stood and looked on her. He knew that she was a Mermaid and that as soon as she awoke she would slip back into the ocean and be lost to him. So he bound her fast with his girdle.

Then she awoke and opened her eyes, which were blue as the sea, and when she saw that she was bound, she cried out with terror, 'Loose me, man, loose me!'

Conchubar did not answer, so she said again, 'Loose me, I beg thee!' in a voice as sweet as the music of Hom Mooar, the Fairy Fiddler.

By this time Conchubar was feeling that he would give all he had to keep her. He answered, trembling, 'Woman, my heart, who art thou?'

'I am Teeval, Princess of the Ocean,' said she. 'Set me free, I pray thee.'

'But if I set thee free,' said Conchubar, 'thou wilt leave me.'

'I cannot stay with thee, Conchubar,' she cried; 'set me free, and I will give thee a precious gift.'

'I will loose thee,' answered Conchubar. 'It is not for the gift, but because I cannot resist thee.'

He unfastened the girdle from her and she said, 'My gift to thee is this: Go now to Culain who is making thy shield, and tell him that Teeval, Princess of the Ocean, bids him to put her figure on the shield and round it to grave her name. Then thou shalt wear it always in battle, and when thou shalt look on my face and call my name, thy enemies' strength shall go from them and shall come into thee and thy men.' When she had said this, she waved her white arm to Conchubar and plunged into the waves. He looked sadly for a long time at the spot where she had disappeared, and then walked slowly to the forge of Culain, and gave him the message.

Culain finished the mighty shield as the Princess had said, and forged also for Conchubar a golden-hilted magic sword, and a spear set with precious stones. Then Conchubar, in his crimson mantle and white gold-embroidered tunic, and armed with his great shield and his mighty weapons, went back to Ireland.

All that the Princess of the Ocean had said came true. When he went into battle he looked at the beautiful face in his shield and cried, 'Help, Teeval.'

Then he felt strength come into him like the strength of a giant, and he cut his enemies down like grass. Before long he was famous all over Ireland for his great deeds, and in the end he became King of Ulster. Then he invited Culain to come and live in his kingdom, and gave him the plain of Murthemney to dwell in.

But he never again saw the lovely Mermaid.

THE WIZARD'S PALACE

LONG hundreds of years ago there was a fine palace on a mountain sloping up from the sea. It was like a palace in a dream, built of shining marble of all colours and having great doors covered with gold.

In it there lived the mighty Wizard who had made it for himself by his spells. But his hatred of other people was as great as his power, and he would not allow any person to come near him except his own servants, and they were evil spirits. If any man dared to go to see the palace, to ask for work or to beg for charity, he would never be heard of again. His friends might search for him, but they would never find him. Soon people began to whisper that some of the blocks of granite near the palace were like the men who had gone up the mountain and never came back. They began to believe that the Wizard had caught them and frozen them into grey stone. At length the Wizard became the terror of the whole island, so that no person would pass within several miles of his palace. The people of that side of the island fled from their homes, and the place was lonely and desolate.

So things went on for three years, until one day a poor man going on the houses happened to travel on that side of the island, not knowing anything of this Wizard. His road took him over the mountain, where the Wizard lived, and as he came near it, he was astonished to see the place so silent and desolate. He had been looking forward to the usual food and shelter, with the friendly welcome, but he found the houses empty ruins and the kindly country people gone. And where was the straw and hay which made such a snug bed in the barn? Weeds and stones were lying thick in the fields. Night came on him, and he walked and walked; but never a bit of shelter could he find, and he did not know where to go to get a bed. 'It's a middlin' dark night,' he thought; 'but it's better to go on than back

—a road a body is used on is no throuble to them, let it be night or not.' He was travelling on the old road over the mountain, going ahead singing 'Colcheragh Raby' for company to himself, and after a long while he saw a light in the distance. The light got brighter and brighter until he came to a grand palace with every window lit up. The singing was all knocked out of him.

'In the name of Fortune where am I at all? This is a dreadful big house,' he said to himself; 'where did it come from, for all? Nobody never seen the like of it on this bare breas' before—else where am I at all, at all?'

He was hard set to get to the door with the blocks of stone lying about like frozen men.

'I 'd swear,' he said to himself as he stumbled over one, 'that this was lil' Neddy Hom, the dwarf man tha 's missin', only it's stone.'

When he came to the big door it was locked. Through one of the windows he saw a table, and supper ready on it, but he saw no person. He was very tired and hungry, but he was afraid to knock at the door of such a fine place.

'Aw, that place is too gran' for the likes of me!' said he.

He sat down on one of the marble seats outside, saying:

'I 'll stretch meself here till mornin', it's a middlin' sort of a night.'

That day meat and bread had been given to him at the last town he had passed through. He was hungry and he thought he would eat, so he opened his wallet and took out a piece of bread and meat, then he put his hand into his pocket and drew out a pinch of salt in a screw of paper. As he opened the paper some grains of salt fell out, on to the ground. No sooner had this happened than up from the ground beneath came the sound of most terrible groans, high winds blew from every airt out of the heavens, lightnings flashed in the air, dreadful thunder crashed overhead, and the ground heaved beneath his feet; and he knew that there was plenty of company round him, though no man was to be seen. In less than a moment the grand palace burst into a hundred thousand bits, and vanished into the air. He found himself on a wide, lonely mountain, and in the grey light of dawn no trace of the palace was to be seen.

He went down on his knees and put up a prayer of thanksgiving for his escape, and then ran on to the next village, where he told the people all that he had seen, and glad they were to hear of the disappearance of the Wizard.

THE ENCHANTED ISLE

under the Irish Sea, fifteen or sixteen miles south-west of the Calf, there is an enchanted isle. Long, long ago it was on the surface of the water — that was in the days when Manannan ruled in Mann—but when Saint Patrick drove Manannan and his men from the island in the form of three-legged creatures, they came upon this isle. Manannan dropped it to the bottom of the sea, and they were seen no more.

Now it is the home of Manannan Mac Lir, Son of the Sea, and he rules it as he used to rule Mann. But once in seven years, when Old May Day is on a Sunday, the isle may be seen. It rises up from the sea just before sunrise, like a beautiful vision, and Manannan looks once more at Ellan Vannin. The hills of the enchanted isle are green, white foam rings it round, and if you are near enough you may see the tossing arms and golden hair of the Mermaids by the water's edge washing their glittering jewels, and hear the singing of birds, and smell the fragrant scent of flowers. But as the first rays of the sun rest upon its highest hills, it sinks into the deep, deep sea.

STORIES ABOUT BIRDS

Two Ravens met once, and one asked the other in Bird language:

'Is there nothing new at you?'

'The white Horse is dead,' said he.

'Is he fat? Is he fat?' said the other.

'Delicious, delicious,' said he.

Then he repented that he had told him that, and called out:

'Bare bones, bare bones!'

OLD Robin Quirk one fine morning was sitting sunning himself before his cottage door, when the Blackbird, living in the Tramman Tree in his garden, flew down, settled near Robin, and began to talk to him in Manx:

'Irree, Robin, as gow smook.' 'Rise, Robin, and take a smoke.'

'Cha nel thombaga aym.' 'I have no tobacco,' said Robin.

'Kionn eh, kionn eh.' 'Buy it, buy it,' cried Blackbird.

'Cha nel ping aym.' 'I have not a penny,' poor Robin said.

'Gow er dayl, gow er dayl.' 'Credit it, credit it,' was Blackbird's bad advice.

'Cha der ad dayl dou, boy.' 'They won't give me credit, boy.'

'Quit eh, eisht, quit eh.' 'Quit it, then, quit it,' whistled Blackbird, flying home and closing the discussion.

'The imperence of sin is in them Blackbirds!' Robin said.

HOW THE WREN BECAME KING OF THE BIRDS

A LONG, long time ago, before you and I were born, the birds of the air gathered at Tynwald from all airts of the wind. The meeting was to settle once and for all the squabbling and fighting among them as to which of them was the cleverest, and it was agreed that the cleverest bird should be king. The sky was black with them, big and little, and soon all had gathered together. Everywhere groups of birds sat-a-row, cooishing, scolding, or sleeping. Some were in fine, black Sunday coats like old Parson Gull, some clad only in work-a-day brown like Poor Brownie, the Hedge Sparrow; but most wore leggings of red or yellow, while the Chough had a new pair of bright red ones. Yellow Tommy, the dandy, was preening himself, swinging on the top of a gorse bush. Old Greyback, the Crow, perched on a rock above him, silent but observant, was eating flitters; and over all, the blue arch of the sky, in which hung motionless a broad-winged eagle.

The Corncrake officially announced, 'Raip, raip' (ready, ready). Then each one got up in his turn to tell of all the great things he could do. The Falcon boasted that he and his mate were worth the kingdom of Mann with all its rights: Lhondoo, the Thrush, sang her best to them —it was a pleasure to listen to her, and for a moment she thought that she would be elected; Flame of the Wood, the Goldfinch, spread her bright plumage; Fork of the Wind, the Swallow, told of her swiftness and travels to warm countries in the south, the Curlew, of her riches—'Let the curlew be poor or fat, she carries a groat upon her back,' said she, showing the mark of 4 which she bears. When the Cuckoo got up, the Meadow Pipit darted out from a group and danced round, calling out his name to draw attention to himself, the little fool, and saying, 'Let every bird hatch her own eggs,' so poor Cuckoo wasn't heard. There was a loud-voiced dispute between the Magpie and the Jackdaw as to which was the best thief. At last little Jinny Wren got up to have her say, after all the grand ones had done. 'Ha, ha, ha,' laughed the Snipe, and all the birds chuckled; but Jinny Wren got the better of them for all that. Says she:

> Small though I am and slender my leg,
> Twelve chicks I can bring out of the egg.

And the birds agreed that Jinny was as clever again as the best of them. But the eagle didn't like it that a little bit of a bird like Jinny Wren should be over him. So he considered for a minute, and says he, middling vexed; 'Birds, it's only right that the best bird on the wing should be king; let's try a heat to see which of us can go the highest.' Hullad the Owl, looked thoughtful, and said: 'I never saw anything yet worth flying for.' But the birds said:

''Deed, it wouldn't be a bad idea at all.' No sooner said than done. Jinny Diver, the Cormorant, gave the whistle to fly, and instantly off they started. Speeding on great strong wings, the eagle led the way, the little ones following, Pompee-ny-Hoarn, Fat bird of the barley, straggling far in the rear. But the Seven Sleepers, the Bat, the Stonechat, Cooag the Cuckoo, and the others, didn't stir—the sleep had fallen on them. The Eagle flew up and up and away, away to the sun, till he couldn't lift a feather an inch higher. Then he peered down into the blue to the birds far, far below, and he let a scream out of him:

'Ta mish Ree ny Ein, Ree ny Ein.'

'I am King of the Birds, King of the Birds.'

But little Jinny Wren was one too many for him there again. She had taken tight hold of him by a feather under his great, broad wing and hidden herself. And as he cried 'Ta mish Ree ny Ein,' she flew on top of his head and called out, 'Cha nel, cha nel, ta mish er-y-skyn.'

'Not so, not so, I'm above him, I'm above him.'

Down dropped the Eagle, and down dropped the Wren, breathless, but King of the Birds.

And that's why the boys go round on St. Stephen's Day to this day, singing:

The Wren, the Wren, the King of all Birds,
We've caught St. Stephen's Day in the gorse,
Though he's small, his family is many;
We pray you, good woman, give us a drop to drink.

THE MODDEY DOO OR THE BLACK DOG OF PEEL CASTLE.

In the days when Charles II was king in England and Charles, Earl of Derby, king in Mann, Peel Castle was always garrisoned by soldiers. The guard-room was just inside the great entrance gate of the castle, and a passage used to lead from it, through one of the old churches, to the Captain of the Guard's room. At the end of the day one of the soldiers locked the castle gates and carried the keys through the dark passage to the captain. They would take it in turns.

About this time one and another began to notice, sometimes in one room, sometimes in another, a big Black Dog with rough curly hair. He did not belong to any person there, and nobody knew anything about him. But every night, when the candles were lighted in the guardroom and the fire was burning bright, he would come from the dark passage and lay himself down by the hearth. He made no sound, but lay there till the break of day, and then he would get up and disappear into the passage. The soldiers were terrified of him at first, but after a time they were used to the sight of him and lost some of their fear, though they still looked on him as something more than mortal. While he was in the room the men were quiet and sober, and no bad words were spoken. When the hour came to carry the keys to the captain, two of them would always go together—no man would face the dark passage alone.

One night, however, one foolish fellow had drunk more than was good for him, and he began to brag and boast that he was not afraid of the dog. It was not his turn to take the keys, but to show how brave he was he said that he would take them alone. He dared the dog to follow him.

'Let him come,' he shouted, laughing; 'I'll see whether he be dog or devil!'

His friends were terrified and tried to hold him back, but he snatched up the keys and went out into the passage.

The Black Dog slowly got up from before the fire and followed him.

There was a dead silence in the guard-room—no sound was heard but the dashing of the waves on the steep rocks of the Castle Islet.

After a few minutes, there came from the dark passage the most awful and unearthly screams and howls, but not a soldier dared to move to see what was going on. They looked at each other in horror. Presently they heard steps, and the rash fellow came back into the room. His face was ghastly pale and twisted with fear. He spoke not a word, then or afterwards. In three days he was dead and nobody ever knew what had happened to him that fearful night.

The Black Dog has never been seen again.

Little red bird of the black turf ground,
Where did you sleep last night ?
I slept last night on the top of the briar,
And oh ! what a wretched sleep !

Little red bird of the black turf ground,
Where did you sleep last night ?
I slept last night on the top of the bush,
And oh ! what a wretched sleep !

Little red bird of the black turf ground,
Where did you sleep last night ?
I slept last night on the ridge of the roof,
And oh ! what a wretched sleep !

Little red bird of the black turf ground,
Where did you sleep last night?
I slept last night between two leaves
As a babe 'twixt two blankets quite at ease,
And oh! what a peaceful sleep!

An old Manx Lullaby.

LONG hundreds of years ago there was a witch in the island who made herself the finest and cleverest-looking young woman in it. Her like for beauty was never before seen in this mortal world. When she went out walking or riding the very birds of the air would forget to sing for looking at her, and her sweet voice would tempt them off the trees to listen to her. Even the animals would stand still till she went by, for her beauty cast a spell on them. And as for the men, the poor creatures, they flocked from all sides of the island to woo her, and when they had once looked on her face they never wanted to leave her. They forgot everything else in the world — all sorrow and care, home and country, till at last everything in the island came to a standstill because the men followed wherever this young witch chose to lead them. Their haggards were empty, for they never ploughed nor sowed, and their houses thol-thans, for they neither built nor mended. They cut no turf and pulled no ling for fires. Their fields were covered with stones, so that the cattle died for want of pasture. and their gardens were full of weeds. There was a strange stillness throughout the island —no children's voices were to be heard any-where. The witch only laughed to see what her beauty had done, and she kept all the men near her by making each think that himself might be the chosen one. If one asked her to marry him she would answer, 'An' maybe I will,' and then she would say the same to the next. So they spent their days in pleasuring themselves. When she had made slaves of the men of the island in this way, she said one day:

'Saddle me my horse, for I've a mind to ride.'

So they brought her milk-white horse shod with shoes of gold, with bit of gold and bridle set with jewels, with saddle of mother-of-pearl and saddle-cloth of blue Tehi Tegi mounted, and the waves of her golden hair flowed down over her dress of shining white.

'I'm going,' said she, 'to the country for the day, and you can follow me on foot if you like.'

She rode and took her way under shady trees and through grassy lanes, where blue-bells and primroses grew as thick as the grass, and the hedges were yellow with gorse. She went on by fields, covered with stones, which were once fine corn land; and on she went at the head of them by lonely little tholthans whose roofs had sunk in on the hearth, and then by spots where houses once had been, now marked by jenny nettles, and an old tramman tree. Her way mounted upwards among hills shining in the May sunlight, and through gills where little streams ran down between banks covered with fern and briar and many a flower, to the blue sea.

At last they found themselves at the side of a bright swift river, and she put a spell on it and made it seem shallow, and as smooth and clear as glass, so that the little stones at the bottom were barely covered. Then, when they were all beginning to wade through it, she took off the spell and the water rushed over their heads and swallowed up the six hundred poor lovers. With that she made a bat of herself and rose up in the air and flew out of sight. Her milk-white horse turned into a perkin, plunged to the bottom of the stream, and swam away out to sea and was never more seen.

From that time the wise men of the island made their women go on foot and follow their husbands wherever they should lead, so that no such accident should happen again. If by chance a woman went first, anyone who saw her cried out 'Tehi Tegi! Tehi Tegi!'

JOHN Y CHIARN'S JOURNEY.

took the biggest journey in his life without meaning to do it at all

One night he was going towards Ballaquirk, taking his time and thinking of his younger days, when all of a sudden he heard a great murmur of people coming up behind him, and, before he had time to look round him, he felt himself getting jostled and a voice asked him—middling sharp, too :

'What business have you here in our way

at this hour of the night?'

'I am sorry to give anyone trouble,' said John; 'I'll get over the hedge out of the road.'

Then the leader came and touched him with the little stick he was carrying, and said to the others:

'We'll take him with us; he'll be useful enough among the rest.'

At that there was a big titter and John felt himself all altered like, and a thing like a load came on to his back. Then they all went on together, Themselves talking and laughing away. As soon as they came near the Ballaragh Chapel though, all was as silent as the grave. The houses were dark and the only thing they saw stirring was Quilleash's dog, and as soon as he smelt Themselves he took to his heels with his tail between his legs.

It was a fine easy night with just a touch of soft fog on, and a little air coming down from the mountain as we got to Dreem-y-Cuschaage. There the leader sounded his big ram's horn, and as they went galloping down to the Dhoon, out came some more of the Lil Fellas from the gill and joined them, and more talking and laughing went on. He blew another blast at Ballellin, for there they could see the fog rolling down from Creg-ny-Molt. Again he blew at Ballagorry and they slacked down a bit, and you would have thought the whole glen would have wakened up with the echoes. Down at the bridge they could see the lights going about like will-o'-the-wisps. Then the leader shouted :

'Get into your lines there, my boys,' and the Maughold Lil Fellas put themselves in rows on the walls of the bridge, just under the big cherry trees, holding their coloured lanthorns on the points of their sticks to give light round that dirty turn; then when all had passed, they joined in and followed behind. Away they all went, down Slieu Lewaige, fit to break their necks. They slackened off a bit as they got to Folieu and then took their time as far as Ballure's Bridge, where there was a big lanthorn hanging up in a tree over the old mill. As soon as they saw this, two of Themselves blew horns and then a host of riders came out of the mill, blowing horns too. They turned up the gill and all of a sudden the whole crowd, with John among them, were right in the middle of a big camp of the Lil People. There were lights hanging all about in the trees, and fires blazing under the cowree pots, and musicians playing fine music. Oh! the taking joy there was! Some were going round, giving horn spoons for the cowree and binjean, and then handing round the oatbread and cheese, and the tramman wine. Then the little fiddlers and fluters and reed-fellows and the drummers got upon the top of a big rock, and the Lil Fellas began to dance, till John's head took the reel watching them. It was a grand sight to see the nice little girls in their red petticoats, and white stockings and shoes with silver buckles on, and little bells all tinkling in their hair; and the Lil Men in their white knee breeches, loghtan stockings and spotted carranes. In the middle of it all, up came the Lil Captain—

'John,' says he. 'What do you think of this sight, boy?'

'It's mortal grand,' says John. 'Far before any of the carnivals I've seen before; an' how long will it last?'

'Maybe a fortnight,' said he, laughing heartily. 'And maybe more, so you would better go back to your own people.'

'How'll I get back at all, at all, an' in the dark, too?' says John.

'Tchut, man,' he said, tipping John on the head with his little stick again.

John didn't remember any more till he wakened at the break of day close to his own house, and little the worse for his long journey.

May the chimney-hook and the pot-hooks
Against thee rise in cruel war ;
The ladle, the dishes, and the pot-stick,
For the dread attack prepare.

May the pot-stick and the round tables,
Cresset, noggin, and hardware store,
All help to tear, and flay, and skin thee
When fell'd beneath them on the floor.

What if the spotted water-bull,
  And the Glashtan would take thee, for all
And the Fynoderee of the glen, waddling,
  To make of thee a bolster against the wall

The Fairy of the Glen and the Buggane,
  Finn MacCool and all his company;
May they gather together about thy bed,
  And in a straw-rope creel run off with thee.

From an old Manx Ballad.

THE WITCH OF SLIEU WHALLIAN

IT WAS Midsummer Day, and the Peel Herring Fleet, with sails half set, was ready for sea. The men had their barley sown, and their potatoes down, and now their boats were rigged and nets stowed on board and they were ready for the harvest of the sea. It was a fine day, the sky was clear and the wind was in the right airt, being from the north. But, as they say, 'If custom will not get custom, custom will weep.' A basinful of water was brought from the Holy Well and given to the Wise Woman that sold fair winds, as she stood on the harbour-side with the women and children to watch the boats off. They told her to look and tell of the luck of the Herring Fleet. She bent over the water and, as she looked, her face grew pale with fear, and she gasped: 'Hurroose, hurroose! An' do ye know what I'm seeing?'

'Let us hear,' said they.

I'm seeing the wild waves lashed to foam away by great Bradda Head,
I'm seeing the surge round the Chicken's Rock an' the breaker's lip is red;
I'm seeing where corpses toss in the Sound, with nets an' gear an' spars,
An' never a one of the Fishing Fleet is riding under the stars.

There was a dead hush, and the men gathered close together, muttering, till Gorry, the Admiral of the Fishing Fleet, stepped forward, caught the basin out of her hands and flung it out to sea, growling:

'Sure as I'm alive, sure as I'm alive,

woman, I've more than half a mind to heave you in after it. If I had my way, the like of you an' your crew would be run into the sea. Boys, are we goin' to lose a shot for that bleb? Come on, let's go and chonce it with the help of God.'

'Aye, no herring, no wedding. Let's go an' chonce it,' said young Cashen.

So hoisting sails they left the port and when the land was fairly opened out, so that they could see the Calf, they headed for the south and stood out for the Shoulder. Soon a fine breeze put them in the fishing-ground, and every man was looking out for signs of herring—perkins, gannets, fish playing on the surface, oily water, and such like. When the sun was set and the evening was too dark to see the Admiral's Flag, the skipper of each lugger held his arm out at full length, and when he could no longer see the black in his thumb-nail he ordered the men to shoot their nets. And as they lay to their trains it all fell out as the witch had said. Soon the sea put on another face, the wind from westward blew a sudden gale and swelled up the waves with foam. The boats were driven hither and thither, and the anchors dragged quickly behind them. Then the men hoisted sail before the wind and struggled to get back to land, and the lightning was all the light they had. It was so black dark that they could see no hill, and above the uproar of the sea they could hear the surges pounding on the rocky coast. The waves were rising like mountains, breaking over the boats and harrying them from stem to stern. They were dashed to pieces on the rocks of the Calf, and only two men escaped with their lives.

But there was one boat that had got safe back to port before the storm, and that was the boat of the Seven Boys. She was a Dalby boat and belonged to seven young men who were all unmarried. They were always good to the Dooinney Marrey, the Merman, and when they were hauling their nets they would throw him a dishful of herring, and in return they had always good luck with their fishing. This night, after the Fleet had shot their nets sometime, the night being still fine and calm, the Seven Boys heard the voice of the Merman hailing them and saying:

'It is calm and fine now; there will be storm enough soon!'

When the Skipper heard this he said: 'Every herring must hang by its own gills,' and he and his crew at once put their nets on board and gained the harbour. And it was given for law ever after that no crew was to be made up of single men only; there was to be at least one married man on board and no man was bound by his hiring to fish in this same south sea, which was called 'The Sea of Blood' from that day.

As for the witch, they said she had raised the storm by her spells and they took her to the top of the great mountain Slieu Whallian, put her into a spiked barrel and rolled her from the top to the bottom, where the barrel sank into the bog. For many and many a long year there was a bare track down the steep mountain-side, where grass would never grow, nor ling, nor gorse. They called it the 'The Witch's

Way,' and they say that her screams are heard in the air every year on the day she was put to death.

THE OLD CHRISTMAS

IN THE DAYS OF our grandmothers, Old Christmas Day, the fifth of January, was believed to be the true Christmas. On Black Thomas's Eve, which was the first day of the Christmas holidays, the spinning wheels all had to be put away, the making of nets ceased, and no work of any kind must be done until after Twelfth Day.

But there was once an old woman named Peggy Shimmin, at Ballacooil, and she was bent on finishing some spinning that she had begun, so on Old Christmas Eve she said to herself:

'The New Christmas is pas' an' surely it's no wrong to do a bit o' spinning to-night.' though she doubted in her heart if she were not sinning. So when Himself and the rest were in bed, she called her young servant-girl, lil Margad, and said:

'Margad, me an' you will finish the spinning to-night.' Margad was frightened, terrible, but she got out her wheel and sat beside her mistress. The two began to spin, and they were spinning and spinning till near midnight, and behold ye, just before midnight old Peggy saw the flax she was drawing from the distaff grow blacker and blacker till it was as black as tar. But Margad's flax did not change colour because she had only done what her mistress bade her. Peggy dropped the flax quick, put away her wheel, and crept in fear to bed. She knew now which was the true Christmas Day and never more did she spin on Old Christmas Eve.

Margad was left alone in the kitchen when her mistress had gone to bed, and at first she was trembling with fright ; but she was a middling brave girl, and she took a notion, as there was no person to stop her, to see if all the things were true that she had heard about Old Christmas Eve.

'They're saying,' she thought, 'that the bees are coming out, an' the three-year-old bullocks going down on their knees, an' the myrrh coming up in bloom.' Then she says to herself :

'I 'm thinking I 'll go out an' watch the myrrh.' So she put a cloak round her and crept out at the door into the cold frosty moonlit night, and midnight had just struck as she put her foot outside. She stooped to look on the spot where the myrrh root was buried, and as she was looking, the earth began to stir and crack, and soon two little green shoots pushed up to the air. She bent closer to see what would happen, and to her great wonder the leaves and stalks grew big and strong before her eyes, and then the buds began to show, and in a few minutes the lovely white flowers were in bloom and the garden was sweet with their fragrance. Margad could do nothing but stare at them at first, but at last she dared to gather one small piece of the blossom, and she kept it for luck all her life. Then she went to the cowhouse and peeped through the door. She heard a groaning sound and there were the young bullocks on their knees, moaning, and the sweat was dropping from them. Margad knelt down, too, and put up a bit of a prayer to the Holy Child that was born in a stall. But the wonders were not over yet, for as she went silently back to the house she noticed that the bees were singing and flying round the hive—they were inside again, when she shut the door of the house behind her.

Always after that, when the neighbours would ask her if she believed in the wonders of the Old Christmas Eve, she would say :

'I know it's true, for I've seen it myself.'

THERE CAME SOME MONKS to the broad, rough meadow which is between dark Greeba Mountain and the high road, and they chose a nice place and set up a church to St. Trinian on it. But they reckoned without the power of the Buggane, who had his haunt in the mountain. The Buggane was mighty angry, and he said to himself:

'I'll have no peace night or day with their jingling bells if I let them finish the building.' And as he had nothing else to do, he took it into his head to amuse himself by tossing off the roof.

So when the roof of the church was first put on, there was heard that very night a dreadful sound in it, and when the people of Greeba got up early next morning they found their church roofless, and planks and broken beams all around the place. After a time, and with great effort, the roof was put on again. But when it was on, a great storm arose in the night and it was blown down from the walls, exactly as had happened before. This fall put fear in the people, for they were sure now that it was the evil, destructive Buggane himself that was doing the mischief. But, though they were terrified, they resolved to make one more attempt; and the third roof was nearly finished.

Now there was a brave little tailor living about a mile from Greeba, and because he had not too much worldly gear, he made a wager that when the new roof was on, he would not only spend the first night in the church, but also make a pair of breeches there. The wager was taken up eagerly, as they hoped that if the roof was one night up, it would be left on.

So Timothy—that was the name of the

little tailor—went to the church on the very first evening after the new roof had been put on. He started just when the shadow was beginning to get grey by the hedges. He took with him cloth, needle and thread, thimble and scissors. He entered the church boldly, lit a couple of big candles, and looked all over the building to see that every thing was right. Then he locked the door so that there was no way to get in. He cut out the cloth, and, seating himself cross-legged in the chancel, he put on his thimble and set to work at the breeches. He paid no heed to the darkness of the lonely church at dead of night, but with long thread and needle he bent low over his work, his fingers, moving backwards and forwards rapidly, casting strange, beckoning shadows on the walls. The breeches had got to be finished, or he would lose his wager, so he stitched away as fast as he could, thinking about the good money the people would have to give him.

The wind was beginning to rise, and trees scutched their arms against the windows.

The tailor looked cautiously up and down and round about. Nothing strange came in sight and he took courage. Then he threaded his needle and began his work again. He gave another sharp glance around, but saw nothing at all except the glimmer of the place near the candles, and empty, deep darkness away beyond them. So his courage rose high, and he said to himself:

'It's all foolishness that's at the people about the Buggane, for, after all, the like is'nt in.'

But at that very minute the ground heaved under him and rumbling sounds came up from below. The sounds grew louder underneath, and Timothy glanced quickly up. All of a sudden a great big head broke a hole through the pavement just before him, and came slowly rising up through the hole. It was covered with a mane of coarse, black hair; it had eyes like torches, and glittering sharp tusks. And when the head had risen above the pavement, the fiery eyes glared fiercely at Tim;

the big, ugly, red mouth opened wide, and a dreadful voice said:

'Thou rascal, what business hast thou here?'

Tim paid no heed, but worked harder still, for he knew he had no time to lose.

'Dost thou see this big head of mine?' yelled the Buggane.

'I see, I see!' replied Tim, mockingly.

Up came a big broad pair of shoulders, then a thick arm shot out and a great fist shook in the Tailor's face.

'Dost thou see my long arms?' roared the voice.

'I see, I see!' answered Tim, boldly, and he stopped his tailoring to snuff one of the guttering candles, and he threw the burning snuff in the scowling face before him. Then he went on with his tailoring.

The Buggane kept rising and rising up through the hole until the horrible form, black as ebony, and covered with wrinkles like the leather of a blacksmith's bellows, had risen quite out of the ground.

'Dost thou see this big body of mine?'

roared the Buggane, angry that Tim showed no fear of him.

'I see, I see!' replied the Tailor, at the same time stitching with all his might at the breeches.

'Dost thou see my sharp claws?' roared the Buggane in a more angry voice than before.

'I see, I see!' answered again the little Tailor, without raising his eyes, and continuing to pull out with all his might.

'Dost thou see my cloven foot?' thundered the Buggane, drawing up one big foot and planking it down on the pavement with a thud that made the walls shake.

'I see, I see!' replied the little Tailor, as before, stitching hard at the breeches and taking long stitches.

Lifting up his other foot, the Buggane, in a furious rage, yelled:

'Dost thou see my rough arms, my bony fingers, my hard fists, my——?'

Before he could utter another syllable, or pull the other foot out of the ground, the little Tailor quickly jumped up, and made two stitches together. The breeches were at last finished, then with one spring he made a leap through the nearest window. But scarcely was he outside the walls when down fell the new roof with a terrible crash, that made Tim jump a great deal more nimbly than he ever did before. Hearing the Buggane's fiendish guffaws of laughter behind him, he took to his heels and sped hot-foot along the Douglas road, the breeches under his arms and the furious Buggane in full chase. The Tailor made for Marown Church, only a little distance away, and knew he would be safe if he could only reach the churchyard. He ran faster still, he reached the wall, he leaped over it like a hunted hare, and fell weary and spent upon the grass, under the shadow of the church, where the Buggane had not power to follow.

So furious was the monster at this that he seized his own head with his two hands, tore it off his body and sent it flying over the wall after the Tailor. It burst at his feet with a terrific explosion, and with that the Buggane vanished, and was never seen or heard of afterwards. Wonderful to relate, the Tailor was not hurt, and he won the wager, for no person grumbled at the few long stitches put into the breeches.

And as for St. Trinian's Church, there is no name on it from that day till this but Keeill Vrisht—Broken Church—for its roof was never replaced. There it stands in the green meadow under the shadow of rocky Greeba Mountain, and there its grey roofless ruins are to be found now.

MAGNUS, great nephew of Olaf the Saint, was King of Norway in the days when the Norwegian Kings were Lords over Mann, and he was called by the name of Barefoot because he wore kilts. He was the bravest and most beautiful young king of his time —tall and strong and brilliant as a meteor. He wore a helmet on his head and carried a red shield with a golden lion upon it ; he had in his belt a sword of exceeding sharpness with an ivory hilt inlaid with gold, and a keen javelin in his hand. Over his coat of mail was a tunic of ruby-red, embroidered with a golden lion. He was a fine and valiant figure. It was he who brought King Olaf's Cup of Peace to our island, and this is the way it happened.

Magnus was sitting at supper one day with his chief men, and their talk ran on the beautiful shrine of Olaf the Saint, which was the wonder of its age. They spake to one another of how it was said that Olaf's body would never be destroyed by death, but would remain as in life and would heal those who prayed at the shrine of any sickness. Magnus laughed the story to scorn and said boldly:

'Seeing is believing; let the shrine be opened that we may see for ourselves if the story be true.'

Then the bishop and clergy were horrified, and begged the king: 'Oh king, let not the thing be done, it will surely bring evil on thee.'

But Magnus commanded:

'Let the shrine be opened at once. I fear no man alive or dead.'

So his will was done and when the jewelled shrine was opened, all saw the body of holy Olaf lying incorrupt and fair as if alive. Magnus touched it with his hands, but was suddenly seized with a great fear. He went away in haste, but took with him the lovely crystal cup that lay beside the Saint.

The next night in his sleep he had a vision of King Olaf, majestic and stern, who said to him :

'Choose, I tell you, one of two things, either to lose your kingdom and life within thirty days, or to leave Norway and never see it again.'

Magnus awoke and called his chiefs and great men to tell them of his vision.

'Oh king,' they cried in fear. 'Leave Norway with all speed, and keep thy life and kingship.'

So Magnus, who was the last of our great Sea Kings, got together a fleet of one hundred and sixty long ships, each with twenty or thirty rowers' benches, and with bows carved in the shape of dragons. He loved the sea, and, like a true Viking, he used to say: 'I will never sleep under a sooty rafter nor drink in the chimney corner.'

Away he sailed to the Orkneys; he conquered them and all the Western Islands, and came to Mann. He put in at Saint Patrick's Isle and went to see the site of the Battle of Santwat, near Peel, which had been fought three days before between the Manx of north and south, The beauty of our island pleased his eyes and he chose it for his dwelling place. He made the men of Galloway cut timber and bring it over to make three forts for him. In one of them, near Douglas, he placed the Cup of Peace, which he knew would be well guarded by the Lhiannan Shee, the peace fairy who never left it.

Then he sailed to Anglesey and made himself lord over it, but he soon came back to the Isle of Mann, for it pleased him best. On his return he sent his dirty shoes over to Morrough, King of Ireland, with this message:

'Magnus Barefoot, King of Norway and the Isles, bids thee carry his dirty shoes on thy shoulders through thy house on Christmas Day in thy royal state, and own that thou hast thy kingdom and power from the Lord of Norway and the Isles. And this thou must do in sight of his envoys.'

When the Irish heard this they were furiously angry and indignant, but wise King Morrough said:

'I will not only carry the shoes, but eat them, rather than that Magnus should ruin a single province in Ireland.'

Then he carried the shoes on Christmas Day as Magnus bade, treated the messengers with honour and sent them back to Mann with many fine gifts for their king, with whom he made a treaty of peace. But the envoys told their master of the richness of the Irish lands and the pleasantness of the air, and Magnus kept it in his mind.

After this the King of Scotland sent a message to him, saying:

'Cease to make war against me and I will yield thee those of the Western Isles that thou canst from the mainland go round in a vessel with a paddle-rudder.'

Magnus made peace on those terms and so the Norse Kings gained the Southern Isles, among which they counted the peninsula of Cantyre, because Magnus, sitting at the helm, caused his great warship to be dragged across the neck of land which joins it to the mainland. His vikings shouted with triumph as they pulled the ship along, with their young king in his red and gold laughing at the stern.

But all this time, in his heart, Magnus could think of nothing but the conquest of Ireland. He sailed to the coast of Down, where he began to invade and pillage. It was on Saint Bartholomew's Day, 1103, that his last battle was fought. The Irish had promised to bring him cattle for his troops the day before, but as they had not come he landed his men and marched them to the top of a little hill on the plain of Coba. From this place he could see all the country round, and presently there appeared a great cloud of dust in the distance. Some of his men said that it was an army approaching, others that it was the herd of cattle. The last were right, and when the cattle had been handed over, Magnus and his men returned towards his ships. It was now the noon of a calm and sunny day. When they reached the marshes, suddenly a band of Irish rushed out from their ambush in a wood close by, and attacked them fiercely.

Magnus ordered his chief, Eyvinder, to sound the trumpet and summon his men around the royal standard. He ordered them to close ranks with overlapping shields until they got to the dry ground where they would be safe. They made their way as far as an old fort, but the Irish pressed them and slew many of them. Then the king called to a chief named Thorgrim :

'Do you, with your cohort, cross the rampart and occupy the hill opposite with your archers till we join you.'

Thorgrim and his men did as they were told and crossed over, but when they were across they put their shields on their backs and fled to the ships. When Magnus saw them he shouted:

'Is it thus you run, you coward? I was a fool to send you instead of Sigurd, who would not thus desert me.'

Magnus fought like a lion, but soon he was pierced through the thigh by a spear. He pulled it out and snapped it beneath his feet, crying:

'Thus we, young warriors, break these twigs. Fight on bravely, my men, and fear no danger for me.'

His men prayed him to try to spare himself, but he said:

'Better for a people to have a brave king than an old king!,

And so saying, foremost in the battle, he met his death.

MANANNAN MAC Y LEIRR

Manannan *Beg* was son of Leirr,
He was the first that e'er had Mann;
But as it seemeth unto me,
He himself was but a heathen.

'Twas not with his sword he kept her,
Nor with his arrows, nor his bow;
But when he would see ships sailing,
He hid her right round with a fog.

He'd set a man upon a brow,
You'd think there were a hundred there;
And thus did wild Manannan guard
That island with all its booty.

The rent each paid out of the land
Was a bundle of green rushes;
And that was on them for a tax
Throughout the country each John's Eve.

Some went up with the rushes to
The great mountain up at Barrule;
Others would leave the grass below,
With Manannan above Keamool.

In this way, then, they lived, I think
Myself their tribute very small,
Without care or anxiety,
Or labour to cause weariness.

Old Ballad.

MANANNAN MAC Y LEIRR, the Son of the Sea, was the first Ruler of Mann. He was a great Wizard, and he was so powerful that afterwards he was looked on as a god. He had a great stone fort on Peel Island, and he could make one man, standing on its battlements, seem to be a hundred. When he saw his enemies' ships sailing, he would cover the island round with a silver mist so that it could not be seen; and if, in spite of the mist, his enemies came near, he would throw chips into the water and change them into ships. He was out walking one day on Barrule, when he saw the warships of the Northmen were in the bay of Peel. And with that he made himself into the shape of three legs and rolled like a wheel down from the mountain top as fast as the wind. It was about low tide in the harbour, and there ran a stream of sparkling water out to sea. Now the banks of the stream were marshy, and by the river-side grew a quantity of sedge with broad, green leaves. So Manannan made little boats of the sedge, a good number of them, and sailed his boats in the stream. And when the little fleet floated out of the harbour, he caused them to look like great ships of war, well manned with fighting men. Then terror seized on the Northmen when they saw the Manx fleet, and they cut their cables, hoisted sails, and cleared away as fast as they could, and Manannan and his island were left in peace. Thus did he keep Mann, and not with his sword, or his bow and arrows.

In his fort he had a great banqueting-hall, where handsome boys made sweet music, and others played games and did great feats of strength. He had a horse called Enbarr of the Flowing Mane, who could travel like the wind over sea as well as land, swift hounds that could catch any wild beast, and a sword called The Answerer, whose wound was always fatal, besides his Magic Branch and his wonderful boat, Wave Sweeper.

He governed Mann well for long, long years. Manx people had the best of good treatment from him, and all the rent he wanted was that each one was to bring a bundle of green rushes to him on the Mountain of South Barrule on Midsummer Eve. The island was a happy place, full of sunshine and all pleasant things, and no person there was old or tired or sad.

Manx men have never forgotten Manannan, and this thousand years our fishermen have prayed to him the following prayer, as they have put out to sea. Even up to the days of our fathers it has been used :

Manannan Beg Mac y Leirr—
Little Manannan Son of the Sea,
Who blessed our Island,
Bless us and our boat, going out well.
Coming in better, with living and dead in our boat.

THE CORMORANT AND THE BAT

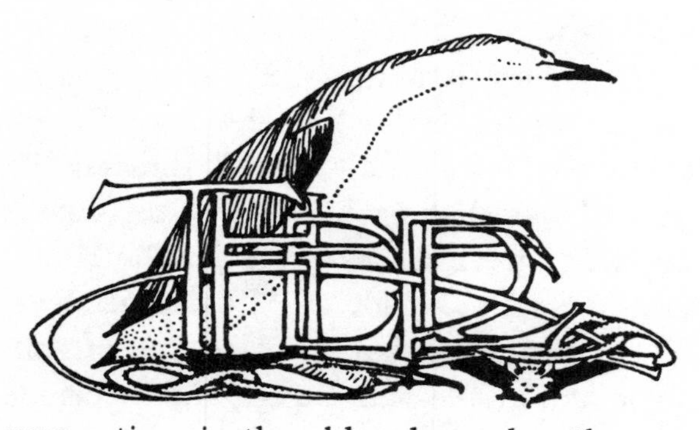

WAS a time in the olden days when the cormorant and the bat took counsel together to do something for the poor, as they had compassion on them, and they went into the glens gathering wool to make clothing for them. When they had a quantity gathered they took a boat and put out to sea. It happened as they were sailing that a storm came on, and the waves were breaking over the vessel, insomuch that the poor bat had to leap from place to place to escape the water, and in the darkness he was cast out of the boat clinging to an oar. At daybreak he was near the shore and flew unto dry land. A seagull, standing near by, enquired:

'Och, lil bat vogh, what's there doin' on thee that thou are all of a thriddle of thrimblin' like this?' When he heard the bat's story, he said:

'As sure as can be, if he will happen on thee, he will take thy life.' They had given each other a promise that one would not leave the other until they had completed their task.

The bat was so frightened that he hid himself in an old ruin until the darkness came on; and from that time until now he will only venture out under covering of the night.

The cormorant held on to the boat until she filled with water and sank to the bottom of the sea. At last he flew to a rock, and there sat for hours together, day after day, looking out for the bat. At other times he would go for a season into the glens; and in this way they continue from that storm to the present time—the one hides himself, and the other seeks him.

OR THE PROPHET WIZARD

In the old days when there were wizards and witches in the Isle of Mann, the greatest Wizard of all was Caillagh-ny-Faashagh. He did not live above ground, but in a quarry, in a hole under the rock on the lonely mountain side, and that is why the people called him the Prophet Wizard of the Wilderness. At dark he would roam over the mountains, and people walking there, when night was drawing on, would hear him crying 'Hoa, hoa, hoa!' like the bellow of a goat, in a voice so terrible and strong that the earth, and all who heard it, trembled with fear. He could change himself into any shape he liked; sometimes he would be a goat with big, fiery eyes; at other times a tall, tall man. Once, when he was a goat, he followed a man that was walking along the mountain road, and that time he had eyes in him as big as two dishes. The man was carrying a lantern, and as he shifted it from one hand to the other the goat followed it from side to side. The man was terrified and began to run. As soon as he left the mountain road the beast roared after him: 'Hoa, hoa, hoa!'

Another time, in the shape of a tall, tall man, as tall as two men, he followed a woman who struck across the mountain at Garey mooar, and he had great, big, burning eyes, as big as two plates, in his head. The woman ran with all her might, for life or death, and he ran roaring after her: 'Hoa, hoa, hoa!' But when she turned down from the mountain he came no further.

He was a great soothsayer, but he would not foretell what was to happen unless some person asked him. It seem that he must have lived for hundreds of years, for he foretold a battle that was fought in 1098.

This was the Battle of Santwat, 'Sand Ford,' between the north and south Manx. He said:

The river Neb shall run red from Glen Crew to the sea,
And the gulls shall sip their full of the blood of Manninee.

It all came true. The north men sailed into Peel and ran their flat-bottomed boats up to Glenfaba Ford, where the south men met them to keep them from landing. They fought up the stream to Glen Crew where there was a great slaughter, and the bodies of the slain dammed the stream and turned the little glen into a pool. The waters of the Neb were reddened by Manx blood when they ran into Peel Bay. The south side women had followed the men and were watching the battle from a little distance, but when they saw that the north people were winning they rushed down, and into the heart of the fight, with bratfuls of stones and with hacks, and won the day for the south. And a law was made that henceforth the widows in the south of the island should get half of their husband's estate;

but the north side women, who stayed at home, were to get only one-third.

The Prophet Wizard foretold, too, the finding of Foxdale lead mines. A man came to him and asked:

'How will I get rich, O Caillagh-ny-Faashagh?'

And the Wizard answered:

> There's a butt in Ballafesson worth the whole of Balladoole,
> But the riches of the Isle of Mann lie hid behind Barrule.

He also gave this prophecy to old Juan the weaver, who asked him for one:

> At the foot of Barrule there will be a market town.
> Mullin-y-Cleigh with blood for twenty-four hours will turn roun'.

Now the village of Foxdale stands at the foot of Barrule, and it is said that in the old times a great battle between the Manx and the Irish was fought by the stream above Mullin-y-Cleigh, the Mill-by-the-Hedge.

To a Peel man he foretold:

'There will be a battle between the Irish

and the Manx at Creg Malin. And the old fisherman say that that battle took place two hundred years ago. It was a Sunday when the Irishmen came in the bay, and they found no place to beach their boats, so they turned the Manx boats adrift, and thought they had the place for themselves. But they soon found their masters. The Manx men came after their boats, and there was the battle—red blood running like water! And the battle was not over that day, but they fought round into Douglas, and finished at last in Derbyhaven, so the old fishermen say.

Then there was an old maid that had a cressad (a melting pot), and she went from house to house making lead spoons. She was a bit queer; she would not smoke a mould on a sunny day, nor a misty day, nor a wet day, nor a windy day; she must have a day to fit herself. She met the Caillagh when he was in the shape of a goat, and she asked him to foretell when would be the end of the world. He said that before the last:

'The Mountains of Mann will be cut over with roads, and iron horses will gallop over them, and there will be an inn on the top of Snaefell.'

That has all come true; trains rush over the island and, for sure, there is the inn on the top of our highest mountain. He said, too:

'Mann and Scotland will come so close that two women, one standing in Mann and another in Scotland, will be able to wring a blanket between them.' But that has not come true yet, though the sandy Point of Ayre is stretching further and further towards the Mull of Galloway.

And another of his prophecies has not come to pass yet:

'The Chief Rulers of Mann will be compelled to flee.'

But it will all be before the end.

THE CITY UNDER THE SEA

where Langness runs its long nose into the sea, and on a place now always covered by the waves, there was once a fine city with many towers and gilded domes. Great ships went sailing from its port to all parts of the world, and round it were well-grassed lands with cattle and sheep. Even now sailors sometimes see it through the clear, deep waters, and hear dimly the bleating of sheep, the barking of dogs, and the muffled chiming of bells—'Nane, jees, three, kiare, queig.' But no man can walk its streets.

For once upon a time, in the days when there were giants in the Isle of Mann, Finn Mac Cooill had his home near this city. He lived at the Sound to keep his eye on Erinn, and to watch the sea. But he was very seldom in Mann, and wherever he was he was always doing some mischief, so that his enemies were many. One day he was in such a hurry to reach his home that he jumped from Erinn and landed in the island on the rocks above the Sound. He came down with such force that he left his footmarks in the hard stone, and the place has been called ever since, Slieu ynnyd ny Cassyn, or the Mountain of the place of the Feet. His first act when he reached home was to get in a red rage with the people of the city close by; his next act was to turn them all into blocks of granite. In his passion he struck the ground so hard with his club that he made a great dent in it—the waves rushed into the deep hollow and the roaring sea drowned the din of the city. Its towers and domes were covered by the green water; its streets and market-place, its harbour and its crowded quays, disappeared from sight. And there it lies to this day.

But there is a strange story told of a man that went down to it more than two hundred years ago. A ship was searching for sunken treasure in those parts and this man was let down to the bottom of the sea in a kind of ancient diving bell. He was to pull the rope when he wished to be let down further. He pulled and pulled till the men on the ship knew that he was as deep down in the sea as the moon is high up in the sky; then there was no more rope and they had to draw him up again. When he was on deck he told them that if he could have gone further he would have made the most wonderful discoveries. They begged him to tell them what he had seen, and when he had drunk a cup of wine he told his story.

First he had passed through the waters in which the fishes live; then he came into the clear and peaceful region where storms never come, and saw the bottom of the World-under-Sea shining with coral and bright pebbles. When the diving bell rested on the ground he looked through its little windows and saw great streets decorated with pillars of crystal glittering like diamonds, and beautiful buildings made of mother-of-pearl, with shells of every colour set in it He longed to go into one of these fine houses, but he could not leave his diving bell, or he would have been drowned. He managed to move it close to the entrance of a great hall, with a floor of pearls and rubies and all sorts of precious stones, and with a table and chair of amber. The walls were of jasper, and strings of lovely jewels were hanging on them. The man wished to carry some away with him, but he could not reach them—the rope was at an end. As he rose up again towards the air he met many handsome Mermen and beautiful Mermaids, but they were afraid of him, and swam away as fast as they could.

That was the end of the man's story.

After that he grew so sad with longing to go back to the World-under-Sea and stay there for ever, that he cared for nothing on earth, and soon died of grief.

THE Night-man lived in a lonely cave, well hid on the side of Cronk-y-Thonna, and he would sit there looking out over the ling of Glen Roy, the ruddy glen, as they were calling it. No person would go near that cave except the most daring boys, and even they had often cause to regret that they had put a sight on the Night-Man's home. Sudden pains would sometimes warn them off, or they would sprain their wrists or ankles. The children out that way after blackberries or hazel-nuts would always be careful to give the place a wide berth, as they would be told to mind for their lives not to go too near. But, for all that, the Dooinney-Oie was useful to the folk of Laxey and the gills around, for he would give them warning of the approach of storms and so save the lines, nets and pots of the fishermen of Old Laxey, and sometimes even the lives of the men. The farmers and crofters, too, had often to thank him that they were able to gather their flocks down from the hill-sides into places of safety. Like the Fyn-oderee, the Night-Man was always ready to help the people in every way he could, and many a piece of work would he do for them while they were in their beds asleep.

Once on a time he took a notion that he could give the warning of storms that were coming on, to more of the people in the gills around, if he could find a way to get on to the breast of Lhergy Grawe, so he took a whole month of planning, and at last he made a big chariot with two little wheels on one side and two big wheels on the other, and with it he was able to go on the sides of the Lhergy without any fear of getting capsized, and he had the seat hanging to the frame on strips of hide to save him from getting bumped going over the rough places on his road. Now he was putting the horses to one end to go, and then putting them to the other end to go back, and that was always keeping his chariot safe. After that, the whole of Glen Roy and the Glen Drink, as well as the Laxey gill, were able to look out in time. The spot where he was making his stand was right on the point of the breast of Lhergy Grawe. It was there he would blow his horn. One time a young man of the name of Joe Steveson was coming home late one still September night, and the moon shining bright on Lhergy Grawe, when he heard the horn of the Dooinney-Oie. He saw something strange shining in the ling on the brow of the mountain. He crossed over the river and climbed up the Lhergy to the place, and for sure there was the bugle horn the Dooinney-Oie was using left behind on the brow. But Joe, after looking well at it, though careful not to try it, was too terrified to carry it away with him, so he hid it.

The Dooinney-Oie came back that night, and when he found that his horn was gone he went into a terrible rage and the noise he made was something to be remembered.

The gills were echoing to his cries like rolls of thunder and the people said that he was that wild that fire was flying out of his mouth. Poor Steveson got such a fright that he never did any more good.

And one night, when the Night-Man had just come to his stand on Lhergy Grawe, a Baldhoon man who had often vexed him by shouting back across the valley, was in the Laxey gill coming home with a good sup at him (i.e. with a drop too much). When he heard the horn he began shouting,—'Save thy wind and go thy ways home!' The Dooinney-Oie didn't mind him at first. Then he said something that made the Dooinney-Oie jump out of his seat and rush down the Lhergy shouting and stamping till he was making the ground shake under him. Hearing the sound coming nearer and nearer, the man got frightened, and took to his heels for his life, knowing now that he was in the way of danger. Luckily for him there was plenty of water in the river, and when the Dooinney-Oie got to the bottom of the mountain he found the stepping-stones covered. He went back up the hill a little bit, then he took a run, gave a shout, made a leap, and over he went. Poor Joe knew now that there was only one chance for him, and that was to get to the house of a religious man that was on his way home, so he took to his heels for all he was worth, trembling with fear, as the shout was coming nearer and nearer. He got inside the house just when one big shout at the door made the scraas (turfs) shake on the rafters, and the thatch rattle as if a shower of hail-stones was coming down. Luckily that was all the harm the Dooinney-Oie could do. Joe stopped there for that night, and took good care never to shout after the Night-Man any more.

Years after this, when the horn of the Dooinney-Oie was seldom heard, a Grawe man took it into his head that the trees growing around the place where he used to come were a hindrance. So he went and made a new road from the Chibbyr-y-Pherick road through the trees, but that didn't coax him a bit. Then he took the notion that the poor Night-Man must be dead, and that, as he was such a faithful old friend of the people, he deserved a monument. So he went and got quarry-men and masons, and they put up a big round tower on the spot. The Dooinney-Oie came to put a sight on it just before it was finished, so he took hold of it and gave one big shout out of him, and tore it every bit to the ground, and from that day to this he was never seen again.

Some say that he will come back once more, and some think that he never will. But on still evenings, when the sun is sinking red into the banks of clouds that lie low on the grey sea, the farmers fancy that they hear far away on Lhergy Grawe the horn of the Dooinney-Oie—h-o-w-l-a, how-la-la!

LONG centuries ago, when Manannan Mac Lir was ruling in Mann, and when his court was famous over all the world for brave warriors and wise men, Lugh of the Long Arm was sent over from Erinn to be brought up there. Lugh was the son of Kian, a great Lord of the Danaan, the people that had the power in Erinn in those days. The boy was beautiful to look on,—his curling hair was the colour of the flower of the broom, and his eyes were blue and flaming as the sword-blade of a hero. Manannan had him trained with his own sons in the use of arms, and he learned to hunt and to fish, to run and to swim. He grew tall and strong, and braver than any young man of his time.

He and the sons of Manannan led a joyous and free outdoor life in the wild places of the Island. There were forests in Mann then, alive with game; there were lakes and rivers full of fish, and curraghs swarming with waterfowl. So they hunted the red deer and the fierce purr in the green woods and the cruel wolf on the mountains. The sound of their hunting horns and the baying of their hounds made music in the dark forest and winding glen, and floated over the the lonely mountains, purple with ling and golden with gorse.

They often put to sea in Manannan's magic boat Wave Sweeper, which carried them wherever they wished without sail or oars; and sometimes they would climb the houghs behind Peel Hill to take the young falcons from their nests.

So the time wore on.

The home of Manannan was not in the Island itself, but in the rocky grey Islet lying off the spur of Peel Hill. When the sun was shining on the summer sea, the Islet sparkled like a jewel on the clear green water. When the sunset was blazing behind it, and the red cliffs across the bay were glowing with colour, it seemed to float like a cloud in the radiance of crimson and gold. Around it the white gulls rested on the water as if they were asleep, or circled round it on flashing wings. At all times the home of Manannan was fairer than words can tell. He had also a summer palace on South Barrule. It was here that he met his people and received the yearly rent from each landholder of a bundle of green sedge. They brought it to him at the Festival of the Sun, on Midsummer Eve, and as they sat on the slopes of this mountain they would weave mats for his palace, for they were clever plaiters of rush. And that is why to this day rushes are strewn on the path to Tynwald Hill on Midsummer Day. From this palace Lugh could see his own country, Erinn.

When the angry winter sea, grey and misty, surged against Manannan's home, and the wind shrieked and whistled over the Islet, the waves flew up from the hard rocks and burst in masses of white spray over the great roof of the banqueting hall. At the fall of day, when the men gathered together by the turf fire on the wide hearth, the roar of the sea was always in their ears. Here they listened to the bards chanting their tales to the sound of the harp, and they taught Lugh to be a great harpist. He had three wonderful tunes—the Laughing Tune, the Sleeping Tune, and the Weeping Tune, which made those that listened laugh, or sleep, or weep, as he wished. He was taught to write in ogams, too, and the rules of poetry. One night, when some of Manannan's fine dark-eyed young men were playing sweet music, and others, lean and well-trained, were casting osier rods, nine at a time, up to the roof and catching them again, Manannan, looking out of his kingdom, saw how the Fomorians were warring against the people of Dana, and making themselves masters over them; so he determined to send to their aid his foster son, Lugh. He called to Lugh, saying:

'Go to the rescue of thy people: we can teach you nothing more. But these Fomorians are fierce and cruel, and I will send you against them prepared as one of your rank should be.'

So Lugh was sent away with splendid gifts,—he wore Manannan's coat, wearing which he could not be wounded, and also his breastplate, which no weapon could pierce. His helmet had two precious stones set in front and one behind, which flashed as he moved. And Manannan girt him for the fight with his own deadly sword, called the Answerer, from the wound of which no man ever recovered, and those who were opposed to it in battle were so terrified that their strength left them. He rode Manannan's horse, Enbarr of the Flowing Mane, which could travel over land or sea as swiftly as the wind. His foster-brothers and Manannan's Fairy Cavalcade went with him, and away he travelled westward over the stormy sea to Erinn.

As he went he looked back at the green hills of Manannan's Island, and he saw his foster-father's noble figure standing on the beach. Manannan was wrapped in his magic cloak of colours, changing like the sun from blue-green to silver, and again to the purple of evening. He waved his hand to Lugh, and cried:

'Victory and blessing with thee!'

So Lugh, glorious in his youth and strength, left his Island home.

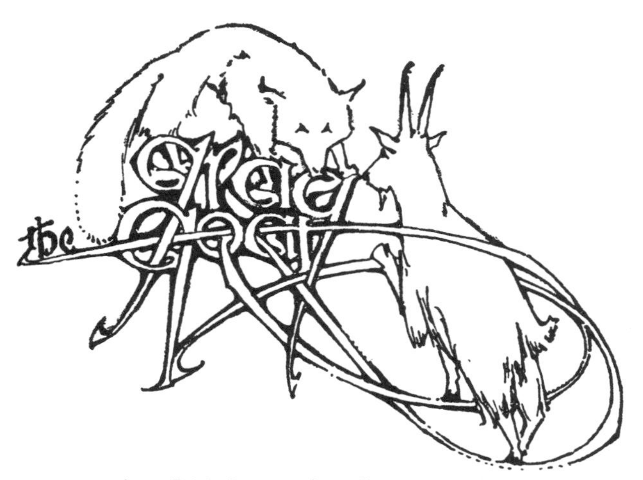

An Old Story for the Little Ones.

CHEAYLL mee myr shoh dy row goayr glass ayn.

As keayrt dy row va goayr glass ayn, v'ee goll un Jeheiney-Chaisht dys y traie dy hymsagh barnee. Ren ee faagail ny Tree mannanyn beggey glassey as yn guilley-bock ec y thie. As dooyrt ee roosyn nagh row ad dy osley yn dorrys da pagh erbee dys harragh ee eehene thie reesht.

'As,' dooyrt ish, 'Tra higyms thie ver shiu enn dy re meehene t'ayn cha leah's nee shiu fakin my chass sthie fo bun ny coolley, son bee snaie jiarg as snaie gorrym mysh my chass.'

Cha row yn goayr glass foddey er sooyl ass y thie tra haink yn kayt dys y dorrys, as dooyrt eh :

'Foshil shoh, foshil shoh, mish dty vummig, mish dty vummig, mish dty vummig.'

'Cur dty spaag veg stiagh fo bun ny coolley, as neem's cur enn ort my t'ou uss my vummig,' dooyrt yn guilley-bock.

Hug yn kayt e spaag veg stiagh fo bun ny coolley, as dooyrt yn guilley-bock :

'Cha nel oo, cha nel oo my vummig ; ta snaie jiarg as snaie gorrym mysh spaag veg my vummig hene.'

Cha leah as ren yn kayt clashtyn shen, hie eh roish.

Tammylt beg lurg shen, quoi haink dys y dorrys agh yn coo, as dooyrt eh :

'Foshil shoh, foshil shoh, mish dty vummig, mish dty vummig, mish dty vummig.'

'Cur dty spaag veg stiagh fo bun ny coolley, as neem's cur enn ort my t'ou uss my vummig,' dooyrt yn guilley-bock.

Chelleeragh hug yn coo e spaag stiagh fo

bun ny coolley, as dooyrt yn guilley-bock:

'Cha nel oo, cha nel oo my vummig; ta snaie jiarg as snaie gorrym mysh spaag veg my vummig hene.'

Cha leah as ren yn coo clashtyn shen, hie eh roish.

Agh cha row yn coo foddey ersooyl tra haink yn shynnagh dys y dorrys, as dooyrt eh:

'Foshil shoh, foshil shoh, mish dty vummig, mish dty vummig.'

'Cur dty spaag veg stiagh fo bun ny coolley as neem's cur enn ort my t'ou uss my vummig,' dooyrt yn guilley-bock.

Chelleeragh hug yn shynnagh e spaag stiagh fo bun ny coolley, as dooyrt yn guilley-bock:

'Cha nel oo, cha nel oo my vummig; ta snaie jiarg as snaie gorrym mysh spaag veg my vummig hene.'

Cha leah as ren yn shynnagh clashtyn shen, hie eh roish cha skibbylt as yinnagh e chraueyn cur kied da, as cha ren eh fuirraghtyn dys haink eh dys thie yn chabbil. Ren eh siyr mooar dy chleiy ayns y thorran, as cha ren eh fuirraghtyn dys hooar eh snaie jiarg as snaie gorrym. Chiangle eh ad my geayrt e spaag as hie eh reesht dys thie ny goayr, as dooyrt eh:

'Foshil shoh, foshil shoh, mish dty vummig, mish dty vummig.,

'Cur dty spaag veg stiagh fo bun ny coolley, as neem's cur enn ort my t'ou uss my vummig," dooyrt yn guilley-bock.

Chelleeragh hug yn shynnagh e spaag stiagh fo bun ny coolley, as tra honnick yn guilley-bock yn snaie jiarg as snaie gorrym urree, dooyrt eh:

'T'ou uss, t'ou uss my vummig,' as ren eh fosley yn dorrys da.

Cha leah as hooar yn shynnagh sthie gow eh greim er ny mannanyn, as hug eh lesh thie marish yn ayrn nagh voddagh eh gee jeu, as ren eh gra:

Oie vie noght,
Laa mie mairagh,
Foolliagh ny shibberagh
Jean eh jinnairagh.

Er-y-gherrit haink yn goayr glass thie voish y traie, as cha row roee agh thie follym. Huitt ee er keayney dy-sharroo son thootchey beg, eisht, fegooish cumrailys erbee roie ee dy yeeaghyn ayns thieyn ny ainjysee eck son ny mannanyn. Haink ee dys thie yn chayt, as ghow ee jeeragh seose dys mullagh yn thie, myr te yn cliaghtey jeh'n keint cheddin dy yannoo.

'Quoi t'ayns shen er mullagh my waag veg screebey-scrabey, screebey-scrabey ; nagh lhig dou broie my hoddagyn ny cloie my hollaghyn ?' dooyrt yn kayt.

'She mish t'ayns shoh, y goayr glass, shirrey son ny tree mannanyn beggey glassey as yn guilley-bock.'

'Er y thalloo ta foyd as ayns yn aer t'erdty-skyn, cha naik mee rieau dty vannanyn,' dooyrt yn kayt.

Hie ee roee dys thie yn choo, as myr ta'n cliaghtey lesh y cheint ghow ee jeeragh seose dys mullagh yn thie.

'Quoi t'ayns shen er mullagh my waag veg screebey-scrabey, screebey-scrabey; nagh lhig dou broie my hoddagyn ny cloie my hollaghyn ?' dooyrt yn coo.

'She mish t'ayns shoh, y goayr glass,

shirrey son ny tree mannanyn beggey glassey as yn guilley-bock.'

'Er y thalloo ta foyd as ayns yn aer t'erdty-skyn, cha naik mee rieau dty vannanyn,' dooyrt yn coo.

Hie ee roee dys thie yn çhynnagh, as myr ta'n cliaghtey lesh y cheint, ghow ee jeeragh seose dys mullagh yn thie.

'Quoi t'ayns shen er mullagh my waag veg screebey - scrabey, screebey - scrabey ; nagh lhig dou broie my hoddagyn, ny cloie my hollaghyn ?' dooyrt yn shynnagh.

'She mish t'ayns shoh, y goayr glass, shirrey son ny tree mannanyn beggey glassey as yn guilley-bock.'

'Er y thalloo ta foyd, as ayns yn aer t'erdty-skyn, cha naik mee rieau dty vannanyn. Agh trood stiagh as gow aash, my neen, as veryms dhyt bolgum çheh. Er-lhiams dy vel oo skee as accryssagh lurg wheesh rouail choud jeeaghyn son dty vannanyn,' dooyrt yn shynnagh.

Myr shen va drogh-yerrey er yn goayr glass, hie ee stiagh ayns thie yn çhynnagh, as tra hooar eh ee stiagh, varr eh ee myr ren eh ny mannanyn, as ren eh gra:

Oie vie noght,
Laa mie mairagh,
Foolliagh ny shibberagh,
Jean eh jinnairagh.

[TRANSLATION]

I heard, as I am going to tell you, about a gray goat.

And there was once a gray goat, she was going one Good Friday to the shore to gather shell-fish. She left the three small gray kids and the little he-goat at home. And she said to them that they were not to open the door to any one until she herself came home again.

'And,' says she, 'when I come home you will know it is myself that's in as soon as you see my foot under the edge of the door, for there will be a red thread and a blue thread about my foot.'

The gray goat had not long gone out of the house when the cat comes to the door, and says he:

'Open this, open this, I am thy mother, I am thy mother.'

'Put thy little paw in under the edge of the door, and I shall know if thou art my mother,' says the little goat.

The cat put his paw in under the edge of the door, and says the little goat:

'Thou art not, thou art not my mother; there is a red thread and a blue thread about the little paw of my own mother.'

As soon as the cat heard this, he went away.

A little while after that, who comes to the door but the hound, and says he:

'Open this, open this, I am thy mother I am thy mother.'

'Put thy little paw in under the edge of the door, and I shall know if thou art my mother,' says the little goat.

Straightway the hound puts his paw in under the edge of the door, and says the little goat:

'Thou art not, thou art not my mother; there is a red thread and a blue thread about the little paw of my own mother.'

As soon as the hound heard that he went away.

But the hound has not long gone away when the fox comes to the door, and says he:

'Open this, open this, I am thy mother, I am thy mother.'

'Put thy little paw in under the edge of the door, and I shall know if thou art my mother,' says the little goat.

Straightway the fox puts his paw in under the edge of the door, and says the little goat:

'Thou art not, thou art not my mother; there is a red thread and a blue thread about the little paw of my own mother.'

As soon as the fox hears that he runs away as swiftly as his bones can go, and he does not stop until he comes to the house of the horse. He makes haste to dig in the midden and he does not stop until he gets a red and a blue thread. He ties them about his paw and he returns to the house of the goat, and says he:

'Open this, open this, I am thy mother, I am thy mother.'

'Put thy little paw in under the edge of the door, and I shall know if thou art my mother,' says the little goat.

Immediately the fox puts his paw in under the edge of the door, and when the little goat sees the red and the blue thread on him, says he:

'Thou art, thou art my mother,' and he opens the door to him.

As soon as the fox gets in he lays hold of the kids and takes home the portion he does not eat of them, and says he:

Good-night to-night,
Good-day to-morrow,
The leavings of supper
They will do for dinner.

By and bye the grey goat come home from off the shore and sees before her but an empty house. She sets herself to crying bitterly for a while, then without any delay she runs to look for the kids in the houses of her acquaintances. She comes to the cat's house, and goes straight up to the roof of the house, as is the custom with her kind.

'Who is there on the top of my little hut scratching-scraping, scratching-scraping; not letting me bake my bonnags, nor boil my soup?' says the cat.

'It is I that am here, the gray goat, seeking for three gray kids and the little he-goat.'

'On the earth that is under thee, and in the air that is above thee, I never saw thy kids,' says the cat.

She goes away to the house of the hound, and, as is usual with her kind, she goes straight up to the roof of the house.

'Who is there on the top of my little hut, scratching - scraping, scratching - scraping; not letting me bake my bonnags, nor boil my soup,' says the hound.

'It is I that am here, the gray goat, seeking for three small gray kids and the little he-goat.'

'On the earth that is under thee, and in the air that is above thee, I never saw thy kids,' says the hound.

She goes away to the house of the fox, and, as is usual with her kind, she makes straight for the roof of the house.

'Who is there on the top of my little hut, scratching - scraping, scratching - scraping, not letting me bake my bonnags, nor boil my soup,' says the fox.

'It is I that am here, the gray goat, seeking for three small gray kids and the little he-goat.'

'On the earth that is under thee, and in the air that is above thee, I never saw thy kids. But come in and rest, my dear, and I will give thee a hot mouthful. Methinks thou art tired and hungry after wandering so far looking for thy kids,' says the fox.

Such was the unfortunate end of the gray goat; she went into the fox's house, and when he got her within he killed her as he did the kids, and says he:

Good-night to-night,
Good-day to-morrow,
The leavings of supper
They will do for dinner.

YN DOOINNEY-MARREY (merman, literally 'man of the sea'), is said to be fond of crabs. An old man in Dalby was one day down on the shore looking for crabs. He got a great number. He saw a merman there before him on the same errand, who had not succeeded in getting any. The merman sang out to him, 'Cur partan dou, Juan,' (give me a crab, John). The old man shouted back, 'Cred t'ou cur son eh ?' (what will thou give for it). 'I'll tell your fortune,' said the merman. On this Juan threw him a couple of crabs, and the merman chimed out to him as he sank into the sea, 'Choud as vees oo bio er y thalloo, cha bee oo dybragh baiht er y cheayn, (As long as you live upon land, you will never be drowned at sea).

It is said that a tarroo-ushtey (fabulous water-bull) lived until recent times in the curragh below Ballalough. Old people, thereabout, tell how they often heard it bellow in the dread hours of night. Its last authenticated appearance was about thirty years ago.

One night two lads, after stealing apples out of some gardens on the Patrick road, made a bee-line for Ballalough to shorten their way home. When they came to Cronk Leannag (or as now pronounced Lammag) something big and clumsy, roaring so as to shake the ground, with 'eyes the size of cups, lit up as if by candles,' came out of the curragh at the foot of the Cronk and made for them. At once, they knew that the thing must be the tarroo-ushtey of Ballalough. So they dropped the apples and fled for their lives to the highroad close at hand. As they reached Ballalough gate the thing gave an awful bellow and plunged into the swamp.

IF any one gets a cut in the harvest field from a scythe or sickle he at once chews a mouthful of ribwort plantain, 'slane luss' (heal herb), and plaisters it over the cut, which stops the bleeding.

It is said that the virtue of this plant was discovered in the following way:

A carrage and tarroo deyll, two beetles who are as everyone knows sworn enemies, ('myr y tarroo deyill as y charrage' is a saying for two that cannot agree) had a battle royal one day on the Dalby highroad. Onlookers observed that when the carrage was sore beset and almost worsted he would run to nibble of this herb by the roadside and run back like a giant refreshed eager for the fray. This was repeated time after time till one of the spectators removed the plaintain, most curious to see what result it would have. When the carrage returned again and found no slane luss he turned on his back and died.

IT is not lucky to leave the bellows on the table, or any fire irons; if this is done there is sure to be a quarrel with somebody before the day is over.

It is not lucky to bring yellow lilies into a house before Easter. If they are brought into a country house there will be no luck with any gosling brood that year. If into a town house it means a bad herring season.

"Fairy flowers," (red campion), should never be brought indoor at any time; if by chance they are, that night will the fairies come for them, and then woe betide the person who picked and brought them in. Their bed clothes will be pulled off them on to the floors and bad dreams and pinching black and blue will be their punishment.

On Good Friday only iron really essential for cooking purposes should be heated, the poker ought even to be put aside and an ash or gorse 'bon' taken to stir the fire. This is done in remembrance that Christ was nailed to the cross with iron.

On Ascension Day it is not lucky to look out of the window, or as far as you could see if you were outside.

It is a lucky sign if, on seeing the first lamb of the season, it is looking towards you; if it happens to be a black lamb, it is especially lucky. You would be certain of success in whatever undertaking you were then concerned. If the lamb looked away from you the reverse would be your fate.

It is lucky to hear the cuckoo the first time if you stand on grass. The thicker and longer the grass the better is the luck. To hear her indoors or on the high-road is a sign of misfortune. The same rule applies to the new moon.

If you happen accidentally to put on some

of your clothes wrong side out when dressing you will be lucky all day, — the nearer the garment to the skin the better the luck.

When eating anything first in its season, —say, a fresh herring, or a new potato,—it is lucky to wish, as the wish is certain to be fulfilled.

S. Patrick's Well on Peel Hill possesses the customary Holy Well virtues of healing diseases, more especially sore eyes. It is said, too, that those who drink of its waters on old May Day before the sun rises, if they should wish a wish, will have their heart's desire before another twelve months pass over their heads.

If a moth flies about you, it is because your sweetheart is thinking of you ; if you can catch the moth by clapping it between your hands you will see your sweetheart that night.

A horse that stumbles and starts is said to see fairies.

A notion prevails that if horse hairs be placed in a stream of water and left there they will turn into eels. I have heard a person say that she affected this transformation repeatedly in a stream at Brack-a-Broom.

SIGNS OF 'STRANGERS' (VISITORS).

IT is said if a knife is dropped, it is a sign that a woman will call at the house that day, if it is a fork a man may be expected. If there is 'a stranger on the bar' (colly or soot hanging to a fire-bar) you may know when to expect the visitor by clapping your hands before the fire, for if the 'stranger' flies off the bar at the first clap he will come to see you that day; if you must clap twice to blow it off, he will come the next day, and so on. If it happens to be a particular fat-looking black smut it is the parson you are sure to have.

WHEN the head of the house dies, the bees must be told of it, or else they will go away and never return. The way to tell them is to rap three times on each hive and say, 'Himself is dead' or 'The mistress is jus' gone,' as the case might be. A confused murmuring of recognition may be heard in the hives in reply. Some people convey the news by tieing a bit of crape to their hives, but to rap is best. One woman told 'Yes yah! all me bees are dead and gone. Ye see, no one give a thought to tell them when me man died, for he went so sudden like that we war all knocked fud-y-cheilley (through others). Bees always sarve ye that way, they tell me, if they are not toul' of the death ; they did me, anyway.'

Bees are said to be fond of noise made by metal ; so it is customary, when they swarm, to clash two pieces of metal together, for then they will stop to listen, clustering closely and not go far afield before settling and this saves the beekeeper much work. If a bee comes indoors it is lucky, so is it to catch the first bee you see in the year, for if you put it in your purse and keep it there, so long will you have money.

Bees also serve as a barometer, for if when taking flight from the hive they fly high it is sure to be a fine day ; if but a few bees come out of the hive and fly low, the day will be wet.

It is said that on old Christmas night at twelve o'clock the bees may be heard humming praises in memory of the Saviour's birth, that the three-year-old bullock kneels down in worship, for Christ was born in a stall and the myrrh comes out in flower. I have heard people say that they have heard the bees and seen the myrrh come out in flower at that time, and that they have picked the bloom and brought it into the house with them to convince any sceptical person who might be there.

There is a curious vitality in popular beliefs. This Manx bee-lore is thoroughly classical. The Greeks conceived a wealth of poetical imagery and symbolism round the bee. They considered the bee a type of the soul. In some of the most beautiful of the Greek myths may be found the association of bees with the idea of death, their pleasure in the sound of brass, or music, and the good omen of their appearance.

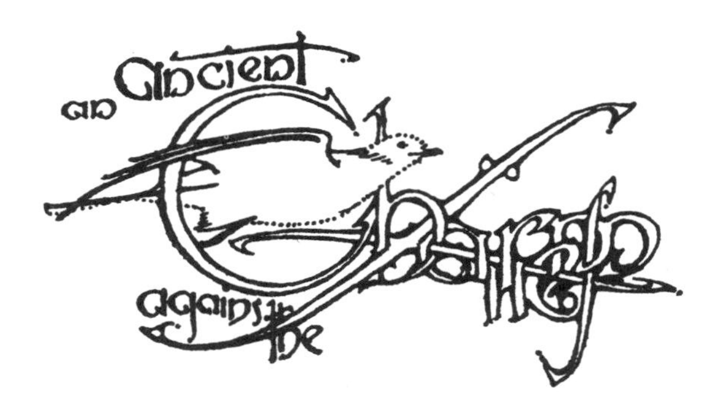

Peace of God and peace of man,
Peace of God on Columb-Killey,
On each window and each door,
On every hole admitting moonlight,
On the four corners of the house,
On the place of my rest,
And peace of God on myself.